GRADING TERMS

A "good" coin is so worn that most of the detail has disappeared. These are not featured: only very rare specimens have any value.

FINE
A coin worn by considerable use, but still retaining clear lettering and some of the finer detail (hair, for example, not just a 'parting').

V.F.
The highest parts of a VERY FINE coin will show signs of its having been circulated. It must, however, possess a pleasing appearance devoid of disfiguring marks.

E.F.
An EXTREMELY FINE coin is almost perfect; close examination revealing traces of wear to the highest parts.

Unc.
UNCIRCULATED - unworn, as struck by the mint.

PROOF
is not a measure of condition, but a description of the method of manufacture. Certain exceptions apart; the field ("unprinted" part) will possess a mirror-like polish; the inscription, legend, or other design, will have a "frosted" appearance; the whole having an effect of great beauty which the smallest scratch will impair.

Excepting rare coins, the value of which is determined by the fact that nothing better is available, to be "collectable" a coin should possess (at least) the requirements of FINE given above. The 'head' should not be worn to a silhouette. The grading should never be qualified by "for its age": a FINE coin of 1800 should be no more worn than a FINE one of 1900 despite the hundred years age difference. The presence of ALL THE ORIGINAL DETAIL but with the highest parts barely flattened (new but 'shop-soiled') would be considered EXTREMELY FINE. Even uncirculated specimens will vie for honours according to freedom from mint bag-marks, brilliance etc., until the rare title of F.D.C. (fleur de coin) is awarded.

MARKETING

It is generally accepted that for the majority of coins a dealer's buying price is about 50% of his/her selling price. The dealer, in effect, is out-of-pocket until a buyer is found. A different 'deal' can be made should the coin be much sought after, particularly if the dealer has a customer in mind. Auction houses attract groups of buyers: collectors and dealers. Advertising, as you would to sell any other commodity, should stress any variety e.g. Obv.3 + Rev.B rather than a bare coin-date-condition. See, also, footnotes on pages 15 and 16.

CLEANING and POLISHING

A dealer's or auctioneer's list will sometimes indicate that a coin has been cleaned; a lower price results: the lesson should be clear. Cleaning diminishes value; polishing will TOTALLY DESTROY.

V.A.T. REGULATIONS: all coins less than 100 years old, whether or not they are legal tender, when supplied by VAT registered persons, are taxable at the present Standard Rate.

COLLECTOI

29th

from 1820

QUARTER-DECIMAL

Copper, Bronze, Silver, Nickel-brass and Cupro-nickel
EVERY non-gold coin from 1820 separately listed for:

GEORGE IV	House of HANOVER	1820 - 1830
WILLIAM IV	House of HANOVER	1830 - 1837
VICTORIA	House of HANOVER	1837 - 1901
EDWARD VII	SAXE-COBURG	1901 - 1910
GEORGE V	House of WINDSOR	1910 - 1936
EDWARD VIII	House of WINDSOR	1936
GEORGE VI	House of WINDSOR	1936 - 1952
ELIZABETH II	House of WINDSOR	1952 to date

ONE HUNDRED and EIGHTY ONE YEARS

GEORGE III · 1760 - 1820 · see page 56

Photographs of coins, and information extracted from its reports, are reproduced with the permission of the Royal Mint.

A compilation of averaged selling-prices drawn from dealers' lists, auctions and numismatic magazines.

ROTOGRAPHIC · 320 Lichfield Avenue · Barton · Torquay · TQ2 8AH

2 QUARTER FARTHINGS FOR USE IN CEYLON

Date	Mintage	Fair/Fine	V.F.	E.F.	Unc/abt.FDC
VICTORIA	YOUNG HEAD			COPPER	13.5mm
1839	3,840,000	£9	£18	£35	£55/£75
1851	Included below	£12	£20	£40	£65/£95
1852	2,215,000	£10	£18	£35	£60/£90
1853	Included above	£6/£10	£20	£40	£65/£95
1853	Bronzed proofs	(from the sets)	---		£250
1853	Cupro-nickel proofs	(P1615)	---		£500/£700
1868	Bronze proofs	(P1616)	---		£250
1868	Bronze proofs	(noted 1999)	"FDC"		£350

THIRD FARTHINGS FOR USE IN MALTA

Date	Mintage	Fair/Fine	V.F.	E.F.	Unc/abt.FDC
GEORGE IV				COPPER	16mm
1827		£4	£8	£20	£40/£60
1827	Proof	---	--		£45 £175/£200
WILLIAM IV				COPPER	16mm
1835		£4	£8	£20	£40/£60
1835	(noted 2000)	"BU Full Lustre"			£125/---
1835	Proof	--- ---		---	£175/---
VICTORIA	YOUNG HEAD			COPPER ·	16mm
1844	1,301,040	£20	£35	£75	£90/£150
1844	RE for REG (P1607)	£100	£250	£750	£950/£1200
1844	Large 'G'	£20	£50	£95	£150/£250
	"BUN" HEAD			BRONZE ·	16mm
1866	576,000	£3	£5	£10	£20/£30
1868	144,000	£1/£4	£5	£12	£25/£40
1868	Proof in cupro-nickel	---	---		£200
1868	Proof in aluminium	---	---		£450
1876	162,000	£1/£4	£8	£16	£30/£45
1878	288,000	£3	£5	£10	£20/£30
1881	144,000	£3	£5	£10	£20/£30
1884	144,000	£3	£5	£12	£20/£30
1885	288,000	£3	£5	£10	£20/£30
	Proofs: 1866 £175;			1868 £200; 1881 £200	
EDWARD VII				BRONZE	15mm
1902	288,000	£1	£3	£6	£10/£15
1902	(noted 1990 Seaby)		---	"abt. Unc" £6	
GEORGE V				BRONZE	15mm
1913	288,000	£1	£3	£6	£10/£15

HALF FARTHINGS ✱ FOR USE IN CEYLON

Date	Mintage	Peck	Fine	V.F.	E.F.	abt Unc/FDC
GEORGE IV	LAUREATE HEAD				COPPER	18mm
1828	7,680,000	Rev A	£10	£20	£75	£120/£200
1828	Rev B see below		£15	£30	£150	£225/£350
1828	Proof		---	---	---	£250
1828	Bronzed proof		---	---	---	£500
1830	8,776,320		£10	£20	£140	£200/£300
1830	Smaller date		£8	£15	£75	£120/£200
1830	Rev B see below		£20	£60	£200	£300/£450
	Rev A: trident reaches above base of letters					
	Rev B: the trident reaches base of letters					
WILLIAM IV					COPPER	18mm
1837	1,935,360		£24	£70	£200	£400/£500
VICTORIA	YOUNG HEAD				COPPER	18mm
1839	2,042,880		£3	£9	£20	£40/£60
1839	Proof bronsed		--	--	--	£200
1842			£4	£10	£25	£45/£65
1843	3,440,640		£2	£6	£16	£30/£50
1844	6,451,000		£2	£5	£10	£20/£40
1844	E of REGINA over N		£10	£20	£40	£120/£250
1847	3,010,560		£3	£6	£20	£40/£60
1851	Unknown	P1597	£4	£10	£25	£50/£70
1851	1 struck over 5		£5	£12	£30	£70/£100
1851	5 struck over blundered number		--		£95	---/---
1852	989,184		£6	£12	£30	£60/£80
1853	955,224		£8	£20	£60	£140/£225
1853	Copper proof		--	--	FDC	£250
1853	Bronzed proof		--	--	FDC	£300
1854	677,376		£10	£20	£50	£100/£175
1856	913,920	P1603	£12	£30	£75	£150/£225
1856	(noted 1995)		"Superb BU full lustre"			£250
1856	Large date		£20	£40 (not distinguished in Peck)		
1868	Bronze proof P1605		(noted 1999) "Virt FDC"			£425
1868	Cupro-nickel proof		(noted 1999) "Virt FDC"			£435

GEORGE IV

Laureate Head · DATE BELOW BRITTANIA · COPPER 22mm

Date	Mintage	Peck No.	Fine	V.F.	E.F.	abt. Unc/FDC
1821	2,688,000 Obv.1	P1407	£2	£9	£18	£50/£70
1821	G of GRATIA over O (Colin Cooke mint 1994)				"Mint state" £69	
1821	Proof In copper	P1408	---	(noted 1999)	"FDC" £380	
1822	5,924,352 Obv.1	P1409	£2	£8	£20	£50/£70
1822	Proof In copper		---	---	---	£350/---
1822	Obverse 2	P1411	£1	£3	£10	£20/£40
1822	"Doubled" D in DEF.		(noted 2001)		"Unc." £36	
1823	2,365,440	P1412	£3	£9	£25	£50/£75
1823	Date has 1 for 1		£5	£20	£40	£65/£95
1825	4,300,800 Obv.1	P1414	£2	£4	£10	£20/£40
1825	5 over 3 (Noted 1993)		£25	---	£45	---/---
1825	D of DEI over U		£10	£50	£120	---/---
1825	Obverse 2	P1414A	£4	£8	£20	£50/£75
1825	Proof In gold	P1415	---	---	Coincraft Cat. £4,000	
1826	6,666,240	P1416	£3	£10	£30	£60/£80

Undraped or Bare Head · DATE BELOW HEAD · COPPER 22mm

Date	Mintage	Peck No.	Fine	V.F.	E.F.	abt. Unc/FDC
1826	Inc. above	P1439	£2	£6	£20	£45/£65
1826	1 for 1	(noted 1995)	£80	---	---	£350/---
1826	1 for 1	(noted 1999)	"Choice EF" £195			---/---
1826	1 for 1	(noted 2000)	"VF" £145	£195		---/---
1826	Bronzed Proof	P1440	---	---	FDC	£160
1826	Copper Proof	P1441	---	---	£60	---/---
1827	2,365,440	P1442	£3	£9	£30	£65/£90
1828	2,365,440	P1443	£3	£9	£25	£60/£85
1829	1,505,280	P1444	£3	£9	£30	£70/£95
1830	2,365,440	P1445	£4	£8	£20	£60/£85
1830	(noted 1999)		---	---	"Superb FDC" £125	

All dies are punched more than once. If one blow fails to register with another, then figures appear doubled, even trebled: this is very common. A major misalignment, however, will add value to the coin.

Obverse 1: Peck says 'the leaf-midribs (if present) are single raised lines'
Obverse 2: The 3 lowest leaves have incuse midribs.

Patterns versus Proofs · If the currency which follows differs then the pattern remains as such. If, however, the currency is based on the pattern then the pattern becomes a proof of that currency. The pattern is a "loner", the proof has "friends".

WILLIAM IV · DATE BELOW HEAD · COPPER 22mm

Date	Mintage	Peck No.	Fine	V.F.	E.F.	abt. Unc/FDC
1831	2,688,000	P1466	£3	£8	£25	£50/£75
1831	Proof	P1467	----	bronzed		£180/£250
1831	Proof	P1468	inverted reverse			---/£150
1831	Proof	P1468	(noted 1999)		"FDC" £175	
1831	Proof	P1469	----	copper		---/£375
1834	1,935,360 Rev.A	P1470	£2	£5	£16	£50/£75
1834	Reverse B	P1471	£2	£6	£25	£60/£95
1835	1,720,320 Rev.A	P1472	£2	£6	£30	£50/£75
1835	Reverse B	P1473	£2	£5	£16	£50/£75
1836	1,290,240	P1474	£3	£6	£25	£60/£95
1837	3,010,560	P1475	£5	£10	£40	£80/£125
1837	7 struck over blundered figure		£10	£20	£60	£120/----

Reverse B has raised line down the arms of saltire
(cross of St.Andrew) (see page 12);
whereas Reverse A has incuse line

VICTORIA YOUNG HEAD

DATE BELOW HEAD · COPPER 22mm

Date	Mintage	Peck No.	Fine	V.F.	E.F.	abt. Unc/FDC
1838	591,360 DEF.	P1553	£5	£10	£25	£45/£65
1838	Variety DEF : on	P1553	£6	£12	£30	£65/---
1839	4,300,800 DEF.	P1554	£3	£6	£18	£40/£65
1839	(no stop) DEF	P1554	£3	£6	£18	£40/£65
1839	Proofs in copper		---	---	---	---/---
1839	Proofs in bronzed copper		---	---	---	---/£180
1839	Two pronged trident (a 'bident'?)			£6	£18	£40/£60
1840	3,010,560	P1559	£3	£6	£18	£40/£60
1840	Variety DEF.. on	P1559	£4	£8	£25	---/---
1841	1,720,320	P1560	£3	£6	£15	£25/£45
1841	Varieties P1560	REG. and REG for REG:	£30			£60/£90
1841	Proof	P1561				£800/£1000
1842	1,290,240	P1562	£10	£25	£75	£100/£150
1842	Variety on P1562	£10 (large '42' in date)				---/---
1843	Struck over 1842		---	---	---	---/---
1843	4,085,760	P1563	£3	£7	£18	£35/£60
1843	I for 1 in date		£25	£50	£150	£300/---
1844	430,080	P1565	£40	£95	£250	£500/£1000
1844	(At auction 1987)	"Mint state"			---	£836
1845	3,225,600	P1566	£3	£6	£18	£40/£65
1845	Large date	"F/gdF" £55		(Colin Cooke 1996)		
1846	2,580,480	P1567	£8	£16	£50	£75/£125
1847	3,879,720	P1568	£2	£6	£18	£40/£60
1847	Proof		--	--	---	---/---
1848	1,290,246	P1569	£3	£6	£18	£40/£60
1849	645,120	P1570	£10	£30	£60	£120/£225
1850	430,080 ?	P1571	£2	£5	£20	£40/£60
1850	5 over inverted 5	?	---	---		---/---

possibly, 5 over damaged 5 (no upright stroke) and much like a 3

Date	Mintage		Fine	V.F.	E.F.	abt. Unc/FDC
1850	5 over 4 (noted 1999)	"nrEF" £35		"Unc" £120/---		
1851	1,935,360	P1572	£10	£20	£50	£95/£150
1851	D of DEI STRUCK OVER ▽		--	£200	£400	£625/----
1852	822,528	P1574	£10	£20	£50	---/---
1852	(noted 1999)	"Almost Unc good lustre"				£175
1853	1,028,628 :					
	W.W. raised	P1575	£1	£3	£10	£25/£50
1853	3 struck over 2	raised W.W.	---	---		£45/£70
1853	Proof, bronzed, with inverted reverse		---			---/---
1853	Proof with raised W.W.	P1577	---			£250/£350
1853	WW incuse	P1578	£4	£8	£20	£40/£60
1853	Proof with incuse WW	P1579	from the sets			£200/£300

FARTHINGS

VICTORIA YOUNG HEAD

DATE BELOW HEAD · COPPER 22m...

Date	Mintage	Peck No.	Fine	V.F.	E.F.	abt. Unc/FI
1854	6,504,960	P1580	£2	£5	£10	£30/£6.
1855	3,440,640	P1581 WW incuse	£10	£25		£55/£9
1855	Included	P1582 W.W. raised	£15	£40		£75/£1.
1856	1,771,392	P1583	£5	£10	£20	£45/£9
★1856	E over R (VICTORIA)	P1584	£15	£80	---	---/--
1857	1,075,200	P1585	£2	£4	£12	£25/£5
1858	1,720,320	P1586	£3	£6	£16	£30/£8
1858	(noted 1998)	"BU Full Lustre, exceptional"				£1.
1858	Small date		£15	£25	£50	---/--
1859	1,290,240	P1587	£15	£30	£60	£100/£15
1860	Obverse date currency	C. Cooke 1990 abt Unc £390				
1860	Obverse date proof	C. Cooke 1990 abt Unc £360				
1864	(Cooke 1993) P1589	Colin not selling even at £7,50				

★ 1856 Also described as R over E. Either R was struck over an incorrect E, or E was wrongly selected to improve a poor R; (or ?): reads VICTOEI...

VICTORIA "BUN" HEAD

DATE BELOW BRITANNIA · BRONZE 20m...
BRONZE = Copper 95% · Tin 4% · Zinc 1
BB = Border of Beads   TB = Toothed Border

Date	Mintage	Peck No.	Fine	V.F.	E.F.	abt. Unc/FI
1860	2,867,200 with various "Berries-in-Wreath" obverses:					
1860	BB 3 berries	P1854	£2	£5	£10	£20/£3.
1860	Proof	P1856	---	---	---	£17.
1860	MULE combining beaded and toothed borders:					
		P1857	£100	£200	£400	£1200/---
1860	TB 4 berries	P1858	£1	£2	£5	£10/£20
1860	Bronze proof		---	---	---	£200/£300
1860	TB 5 berries	P1859	£1	£3	£6	£18/£2.
1860	(noted 1996)	P1859	---	"Full lustre"		£2.
1861	8,601,600 4 berries	P1860	£1	£2	£8	£16/£2.
1861	Bronze proof	(Cooke 1998)	---	"FDC"		---/£23.
1861	Obv. 3 (5 berries)		£1	£2	£6	£12/£2.
1861	Date has small '8'		£2	£4	£12	£25/---
1862	14,336,000	P1865	£1	£2	£4	£12/£2.
1862	Proof		---	---	£200	---/---
1862	Large 8 over small 8	(1990)		£30		---/---
1863	1,433,600	P1867	£15	£30	£60	£125/£20.
1864	2,508,800 serif 4	P1869	£2	£6	£10	£20/£40
1864	plain 4		---	£9	£15	£30/£50

HARINGTON and LENNOX farthing tokens are to be found in "Collectors' Coins: Ireland" (they feature the 'Irish' harp).
From James I to Charles I there were Richmond rounds, Transitional, Maltravers rounds, Richmond ovals and Maltravers ovals

VICTORIA (continued)
DATE BELOW BRITANNIA · BRONZE 20mm

Date	Mintage	Peck	Fine	V.F.	E.F.	abt. Unc/FDC
1865	4,659,200	P1873	£2	£5	£15	£25/£35
1865	5 over 2	P1872A	£3	£8	£20	£40/£75
1865	5 over 3		£4	£8	£20	£35/£55
1865	Date has small '8'		£2	£8	£16	£32/---
1866	3,584,000	P1875	£1	£3	£12	£20/£30
1866	widely spaced 6s		£1	£3	£9	£18/£30
1867	5,017,600	P1878	£1	£3	£8	£18/£35
1867	Bronzed proof	P1879	copper	---	"FDC"	£325
1868	4,851,208	P1881	£1	£3	£8	£18/£35
1868	Bronze proof	P1882	---	---	---	£145/£250
1868	Cu-nickel proof	P1883	---	---	"FDC"	£425
1869	3,225,600	P1884	£2	£6	£22	£40/£65
1872	2,150,400	P1885	£1	£3	£6	£20/£30
1873	3,225,620	P1886	£1	£2	£5	£15/£25
1873	Low set 3 in date		£1	£5	£10	£20/£36

Proofs also occur for 1861, 1862, 1863, 1866.

OBVERSE 4 'AGED' (MATRONLY) BUST still 'BUN' HEAD
'H' (centred below date) = Heaton Mint

Date	Mintage	Peck	Fine	V.F.	E.F.	abt. Unc/FDC
1874H	3,584,000	P1887	£1	£3	£12	£20/£35
1874H	Bronze proof	(noted 1991)	"about FDC"			---/£170
1874H	Gs struck over ⊙⊙		£50	£120	£240	£425/£600
1875	712,760	P1890	£5	£10	£22	£60/£85
1875	8 struck over 8			---	---	---/---
1875	Large date	(5 berries)	£5	£12	£25	£65/£90
1875	Small date	(5 berries)	£6	£22	£45	£100/£300
1875	Small date	(4 berries)	£5	£25	£50	£175/£350
1875H	6,092,800	P1892	25p	75p	£5	£15/£25
1875H	(noted 1999)	5 over 2	---	---	£50	---/---
1875H	RF.G for REG		£1	£2	£5	£20/£30
1876H	1,175,200	P1894	£4	£9	£25	£60/£100
1876H	Large 6 in date		£10	£25	£60	£100/----
1876H	RF.G for REG		£5	£15	£60	£120/----
1877	Proofs only	P1895	bronze	(Cooke '98)		£2250
1878	4,008,540	P1896	£1	£2	£5	£15/£30
1878	(exaggerated)	date spacing variety	---	---		---/---
1878	Proof	P1897	---	---	---	--/£325
1879	3,977,180	P1898	£1	£2	£5	£15/£30
1879	Date has large '9'		£1	£4	£8	£20/£40
1880	1,842,710	4 berries P1899	£1	£3	£9	£25/£35
1880	3 berries	P1901	£10	£40	£60	£100/---

VICTORIA
continued - mainly obverse 5 - BRONZE

Date	Mintage	Peck	Fine	V.F.	E.F.	abt. Unc/FDC/FDC
1881	See below Obv.4	P1901A	£20	£30	£40	£60/£80/£120
1881	3,494,670 Obv.5	P1902	£1	£2	£10	£20/£30/£45
1881	Colin Cooke lists seven "easily determined" varieties for Obv.5					
1881H	1,792,000	P1904	£1	£3	£6	£12/£22/£35
1882H	1,792,000	P1905	£1	£2	£7	£14/£25/£40
1882H	1882H and 1883 have damaged die varieties					
1883	1,128,680	P1907	£2	£4	£16	£30/£45/£60
1884	5,782,000	P1909	£1	£2	£3	£6/£10/£25
1885	5,442,308	P1911	£1	£2	£4	£8/£15/£30

Proofs, in bronze, for all except 1876H and 1879.

Date	Mintage	Peck	Fine	V.F.	E.F.	abt. Unc/FDC/FDC
1886	7,767,790	P1913	---	£1	£2	£6/£12/£20
1887	1,340,800	P1915	£1	£3	£7	£16/£30/£45
1888	1,887,250	P1916	£1	£3	£6	£10/£20/£30
1890	2,133,070	P1917	£1	£3	£6	£10/£20/£30
1891	4,959,690	P1919	£1	£2	£5	£10/£20/£30
1892	887,240	P1921	£5	£10	£20	£40/£60/£80
1893	3,904,320	P1923	£1	£2	£4	£8/£12/£25
1893	Narrower date		£2	£5	£12	£25/£50/£70
1894	2,396,770	P1924	£1	£3	£6	£12/£20/£30
1895	2,852,852	P1925	£6	£12	£25	£60/£90/£150

Proofs occur except 1881H, 1887, 1888,1893, 1895.

'Old' or 'Widow' Head

Date	Mintage	Peck	Fine	V.F.	E.F.	abt. Unc/FDC/FDC
1895	Inc above	P1958	50p	£1	£3	£6/ £9/£18
1896	3,668,610	P1959	50p	£1	£3	£6/ £9/£18
1896	(noted 2000)	"Full lustre, quite superb"				£20
1897	4,579,800:	blackened to distinguish from half-sovereign				
1897	Undarkened	P1961	£1	£3	£6	£10/£20/£40
★ 1897	Horizon as P1961 but black finish				£6	£12/£18/£24
★★ 1897	Higher horizon P1962	50p	£2	£6	£12/£18/£24
1898	4,010,080	P1963	50p	£2	£6	£12/£18/£24
1899	3,864,616	P1964	50p	£2	£4	£8/£12/£18
1900	5,969,317	P1965	50p	£1	£3	£6/ £9/£12
1901	8,016,459	P1966	50p	£1	£3	£6/ £9/£12

Proofs occur for 1896 and, possibly, for 1901

Obverse 4 has 4 berries in wreath arranged as two pairs (2+2 not 1+2+1 as before). Obverse 5 has 3 berries arranged 2+1.

★ Rev A 7 points *TO* a border tooth
★★ Rev B 7 points *BETWEEN* two teeth

EDWARD VII

Date	Mintage		Fine	V.F.	E.F.	abt. Unc./FDC
						BRONZE · 20mm
1902	Type A · weak strike · patchy breastplate					
1902	Type B · well struck · clear design work					
1902	5,125,120	Type A	25p	£2	£8	£16/£25
1902	incl. above	Type B	25p	£1	£4	£8/£12
1903	5,331,200	low horizon	60p	£3	£6	£10/£18
1904	3,628,800		£1	£3	£7	£12/£18
1905	4,076,800		50p	£3	£7	£12/£20
1906	5,340,160		25p	£3	£7	£12/£20
1907	4,399,360		25p	£3	£7	£12/£20
1908	4,264,960		20p	£2	£6	£10/£15
1909	8,852,480		20p	£2	£6	£10/£15
1910	2,598,400		£1.50	£3	£8	£16/£24

All chemically darkened to avoid confusion with gold.

> ★ 1911 The 'standard' Peck obverse 1 has two variations:
> Obverse 1a = above B.M. the neck is hollow.
> Obverse 1b = above B.M. the neck is flat.

GEORGE V   CHEMICALLY DARKENED until 1918 · BRONZE 20mm

Date	Mintage		Fine	V.F.	E.F.	abt. Unc/FDC/FDC
1911	5,196,800	★ 1a	25p	£1	£4	£8/£12/£16
1911		★ 1b	25p	£1.50	£6	£12/£16/£20
1912	7,669,760			50p	£2	£4/£6/£10
1913	4,184,320			65p	£2	£4/£6/£8
1914	6,126,988	BRITT obv 1		£1	£3	£6/£9/£14
1914		BRIT T obv 2		65p	£3	£6/£9/£14
1915		BRITT		£60	"Guesstimate"	---/---/---
1915	7,129,254	BRIT T		65p	£5	£10/£15/£20
1915	(noted 1998)			---	"Finest Unc."	£16
1916	10,993,325			40p	£3	£6/£9/£12
1917	21,434,844			15p	£2	£3/£6/£9
1918	19,362,818	left bright		15p	£2	£3/£4/£6
1918	Rare darkened finish			---	£6	£10/£15/£20
1919	15,089,425			20p	£2	£4/£8/£10
1920	11,480,536			20p	£2	£6/£9/£12
1921	9,469,097			20p	£2	£3/£4/£6
1922	9,956,983			20p	£2	£4/£8/£12
1923	8,034,457			25p	£2	£3/£5/£10
1924	8,733,414			25p	£1	£3/£6/£9
1925	12,634,697			20p	£2	£4/£6/£8
1926	9,792,397			20p	£1	£2/£5/£8
1927	7,868,355			20p	£1	£2/£4/£6
1928	11,625,600			15p	£1	£2/£4/£6
1929	8,419,200			25p	£1	£2/£3/£4
1930	4,195,200			25p	£1	£2/£4/£6
1930	Bronze proof			(noted 2000) "As struck" £200		
1931	6,595,200			25p	£1	£2/£4/£6
1931	Bronze proof	(Peck 2347)	(noted 2000)			/£165
1932	9,292,800			25p	£1	£2/£4/£6
1932	Bronze proof	(noted 1999)		"Superb FDC"		/£175
1933	4,560,000			25p	£1	£2/£4/£6
1933	Proof	(Peck 2353)		---	---	£195
1934	3,052,800			25p	£1	£4/£6/£9
1934	Proof	(Peck 2355)	(1993)	"Stunning FDC"		£195
1935	2,227,200			£1	£3	£9/£18/£25
1936	9,734,400	posthumous issue		20p	£1	£2/£4/£6
1936	Bronze proof	(noted 2000)		"FDC"		£300

'Fine' are sold, usually from 'The Tray' 5p to 25p

✗

> The Modified Effigy was used from 1926 (see page 26)

EDWARD VIII   Duke of Windsor
1937   Extremely rare · not issued for general circulation. £12,000

Date	Details	Peck No.	V.F.	E.F.	abt. Unc/FDC/FDC
GEORGE VI					**BRONZE · 20mm**
1937	8,131,200	---	---	30p	60p/ £1/ £2
1937	26,402 proofs		---	---	£3/ £4/ £6
1938	7,449,600	---	20p	50p	£3/ £6/ £9
1939	31,440,000	---	---	15p	40p/80p/ £1
1940	18,360,000	---	---	25p	80p/ £2/ £3
1941	27,312,000	---	---	20p	60p/£1.5p/£2.5
1942	28,857,600	---	---	20p	60p/ £1/ £2
1943	33,345,600	---	---	20p	60p/£1.5p/£2.5
1944	25,137,600	---	---	15p	60p/ £1/ £2
1945	23,736,000	---	---	20p	50p/ £1/ £2
1946	23,364,800	---	---	15p	60p/ £1/ £2
1946	Bronze proof P2476 (possibly 3 only) (1999)				£230
1947	14,745,600	---	---	15p	60p/ £1/ £2
1948	16,622,400	---	---	15p	60p/ £1/ £2
1948	Bronze proof P2480 (1999) "abt FDC"				£180
1949	8,424,000	---	---	20p	75p/ £2/ £3
1949	Bronze proof (1994) "One of possibly 3 or 4"				£225
1950	10,324,800	---	---	15p	40p/80p/ £1
1950	17,513 proofs		---	---	£3/ £5/ £7
1951	14,016,000	---	---	---	40p/80p/ £1
1951	20,000 proofs		---	---	£3/ £5/ £7
1952	5,251,200	---	---	20p	60p/ £1/ £2
1952	Bronze proof P2488	---	---	---	---/£125/£175
1952	Bronze proof (1998) "Choice FDC, extremely rare"				£185

Proofs for all dates, those not listed are rarely seen; "guesstimate" £250

Date	Details	Peck No.	V.F.	E.F.	abt. Unc/FDC/FDC
ELIZABETH II					**BRONZE · 20mm**
1953	6,131,037 :				
1953	Obv.1 Rev. A	P2520	Currency Set		£1 /£1.50/ £2
1953	Obv.1 Rev. B	P2520A	---	£2	£8 /£16/£20
1953	Obv.2 Rev. A	P2520B	---	£3	£15/£25/£35
1953	Obv.2 Rev. B	P2521	---	10p	50p/ £1/£1.50
1953	40,000 proofs	P2522 (of P2521)			£3/ £5/ £7
1953	Proofs 2 + A	---	---	---	£40/£60/£80
1954	6,566,400	---	---	15p	30p/60p/ £1
1955	5,779,200	---	---	20p	40p/80p/ £2
1955	(noted 1999) "By/Buy the Bag"				
	Colin Cooke offered 2,500 1955s "little beauties" £750				
1955	(noted 2000)			"500 little beauties"	£190
1956	1,996,800	---	---	50p	£1/£1.50/£3

Obverse 1 is poorly defined · the cross points TO a border bead.
Obverse 2 is sharper · the cross points BETWEEN two border beads.
Reverse A (dies of George VI) · 'F' points BETWEEN two beads.
Reverse B is similar but the 'F' points TO a border bead.

1953 Obverse/Reverse Rarity Scale   1 + A (C)   2 + A (ER)
                                      1 + B (R)   2 + B (VC)

(ER) = Extremely Rare · (R) = Rare · (C) = Common · (VC) = Very Common

"POINTINGS" are very much the key to some varieties. A principal feature such as a letter or ornament is selected and its 'attitude' is used to indicate the use of a different die-punch. Thus HALFPENNY indicates that the upright of the 'L' is *pointing* to a rim bead. HALFPENNY that 'L' points between two beads. Many dies are used to complete a full year's striking. New dies are usually identical being from the same, original punch. Differences are, therefore, interesting nusmismatically and unequal strikings must, eventually, show up in valuations.

GEORGE IV

LAUREATE HEAD · COPPER 28mm

Date	Mintage		Fine	V.F.	E.F.	abt. Unc/FDC.
1825	215,040		£10	£40	£100	£175/£225
1825	Proof		--	--	--	£150/£300
1826	9,031,630	Rev A	£6	£15	£45	£75/£95
1826	Proof	Rev A	--	--	---	----/£250
1826	Proof	Rev A bronzed			---	----/£180
1826		Rev B	£8	£20	£60	£120/£180
1826	Proof	Rev B	--	--	£75	£200/£300
1826	Proof	Rev B bronzed			---	----/£180
1827	5,376,000		£8	£20	£60	£90/£125

Rev A; Saltire of shield has two incuse lines P1433
Rev B; Saltire of shield has one raised line P1436
Saltire / St. Andrew's cross, often divided by line/s. (See page 12)

WILLIAM IV

BARE HEAD · COPPER 28mm

Date	Mintage	Fine	V.F.	E.F.	abt. Unc/FDC.
1831	806,400	£4	£10	£45	£95/£125
1831	Proofs, bronzed	head/tail reversed ↓			£200/----
1831	Proofs, bronzed	head/tail upright ↑			£300/----
1834	537,600	£4	£10	£45	£95/£125
1837	349,400	£3	£8	£35	£80/£120

VICTORIA

YOUNG HEAD · DATE BELOW HEAD · COPPER 28mm

Date	Mintage	Fine	V.F.	E.F.	abt. Unc/FDC.
1838	456,960	£2	£5	£25	£60/£95
1839	Proofs, bronzed	---	---	---	£125/£250
1839	Proofs, bronzed, inverted reverse, from sets				£120/£225
1841	1,075,200	£2	£5	£20	£45/£75
1841	Ordinary issue, inverted reverse	£25		£100	£225/£350
1841	Proofs, bronzed	---	---	---	£90/---
1841	Proof, in silver, on thick flan (2.8mm) "guesstimate"				£2000
1843	967,680	£18	£30	£75	£125/£175
1844	1,075,200	£3	£7	£30	£60/£100
1845	1,075,200	£35	£75	£250	£350/£475
1846	860,160	£4	£9	£40	£70/£95
1847	752,640	£4	£10	£45	£90/£135
1848	322,560	£10	£30	£90	£270/----
1848★	8 struck over 7	---	£7	£25	£50/£75
1848	8 struck over 3	---	£12	£30	---/---
1851	215,040 (no dots)	---	£6	£25	£50/£75
1851	Shield, 7 incuse dots	---	£12	£50	£100/£150
1852	637,056 (no dots)	---	£6	£25	£50/£75
1852	Shield, 7 incuse dots	---	£12	£50	£100/£150
1853	1,559,040	£2	£5	£10	£25/£45
1853	3 over 2	£9	£18	£40	£80/£120
1853	Proofs, bronzed, inverted reverse			---	£200/£300
1853	Copper proof	---	---	FDC	£175
1854	12,354,048 ?	£3	£6	£15	£25/£50
1855	1,455,837	£3	£6	£20	£60/£80
1856	1,942,080	£4	£9	£40	£80/£120
1857	1,182,720 (no dots)	---	£12	£50	£100/£150
1857	Shield, 7 incuse dots	---	£6	£25	£75/£125
1858	2,472,960	£2	£5	£20	£40/£75
1858	Smaller date	£2	£6	£30	£60/£90
1858	last 8 over 6	£4	£8	£25	£50/£75
1858	last 8 over 7	£3	£6	£20	£40/£65
1858	'Unrecorded' copper proof	---	---		£125/----
1859	1,290,340	£8	£15	£45	£150/£200
1859	9 struck over 8	£6	£12	£40	£95/£130
1860★★	Extremely rare	£200	£500	£2500	£4000

★ Variety more common than correctly dated piece
★★ Date is below head, not below Britannia

Date	Mintage	Fine	V.F.	E.F.	abt. Unc/FDC.

VICTORIA

"Bun" Head · DATE BELOW BRITANNIA · BRONZE 26mm

TYPE 1 · BEADED BORDERS:

1860	1 + A (P1750)	£1	£5	£20	£40/£50
1860	noted (Cooke 1999) "BU full lustre"		- - -		£48
1860	1 + A (P1751/52/53):				
	Proofs bronze and bronzed £450 to £650				
1860	A "mule" Type1/Type2	£1000		(Coincraft 1995)	

TYPE 2 · TOOTHED BORDERS:

Obv 2 has 7 berries. Obv 3 has 4 berries, all leaves have raised mid-ribs.
Obv 4 has 4 berries, but four leaves have double incuse lines to mid-ribs.
Lighthouse : B tapering, pointed C cylindrical with rounded top.

1860	2 + B (P1754)	£1	£5	£20	£50/£80
1860	3 + B (P1756)	£1	£6	£25	£75/£100
1860	3 + C (P1757)	£1	£6	£25	£75/£100
1860	4 + B (P1758)	£4	£12	£30	£90/£120
1860★	F of HALF struck over P				
	"VF" $60 (£25 1987) (The Rawcliffe Halfpenny)				
1860	(noted 1997)	£25	£60	- - -	- - -/- - -
1861	54,118,400 Ten obv/rev combinations + proofs				
1861	Without signature	£1	£3	£15	£25/£40
1861	Signature on rock	£1	£4	£20	£50/£85
1862	61,107,200:				
	L.C.W. on rock	£1	£3	£10	£20/£30
1862	Proof P1775	- -	- -	- - -	£200
1862	No L.C.W. P1776	- -	£2	£8	£15/£25
1862	Proof P1777	- -	- - -	£200	- - -
1862	A, B, or C to left of lighthouse				£360/£500
1862	Unbarred A i.e Λ £120	- - -	- - -	- - -/- - -	

★ FARTHINGS of this date bear Fs with little or no lower serif to the lower horizontal bar (illustr.) Perhaps the first halfpennies were struck with the same, or a similar, type-face and were overstruck to avoid having HALP PENNYs as well as PARTHINGS.

Date	Mintage	Fine	V.F.	E.F.	abt. Unc/FDC.
1863	15,948,800	£1	£5	£20	£45/£60
1864	537,600	£4	£9	£30	£60/£90
1865	8,064,000	£4	£12	£45	£90/£125
1865	5 over 3	£30	£90	£190	£360/£450
1866	2,508,800	£4	£10	£35	£70/£105
1867	2,508,806	£5	£12	£45	£90/£140
1868	3,046,400	£4	£10	£40	£80/£120
1868	Cupro-nickel proof	(noted 1993)			"FDC" £325
1869	3,225,600	£5	£25	£75	£150/£225
1870	4,350,739	£4	£9	£30	£60/£90
1871	1,075,280 ?	£15	£45	£145	£300/£450
1872	4,659,410	£1	£4	£24	£36/£55
1873	3,404,880	£2	£10	£35	£75/£100
1874	1,347,665	£4	£20	£65	£200/£250
1874	Portrait as 1874H	£1	£4	£24	£35/£55
1874H	5,017,600	£1	£5	£25	£50/£70
1874H	Proof	(noted 1993)			"FDC" £150
1875	5,430,815	£1	£2	£16	£35/£55
1875H	1,254,400	£3	£6	£30	£60/£80
1876H	6,809,600	£1	£4	£25	£45/£65
1877	5,209,505	£1	£2	£16	£35/£55
1878	1,425,535	£3	£12	£36	£85/£150
1879	3,582,545	£1	£5	£20	£40/£60
1880	2,423,465	£2	£5	£20	£40/£60
1881	2,007,515	£2	£5	£20	£40/£60
1881H	1,792,000	£1	£3	£15	£30/£50
1882H	4,480,000	£1	£3	£15	£30/£50
1883	Portrait as 1874 to 1882H	£15	£45		£90/- - -
1883	3,000,725	£3	£6	£25	£50/£75
1884	6,989,580	£1	£2	£12	£25/£40
1885	8,600,574	£1	£2	£12	£25/£40
1886	8,586,155	£1	£2	£10	£25/£40
1887	10,701,305	£1	£2	£9	£25/£40
1888	6,814,070	£1	£3	£12	£25/£40
1889	7,748,234	£1	£2	£12	£25/£40
1889	9 over 8	£8	£30	£90	£180/£260
1890	11,254,235	£1	£2	£10	£25/£45
1891	13,192,260	£1	£2	£10	£25/£40
1892	2,478,335	£2	£3	£10	£25/£45
1893	7,229,344	£1	£2	£9	£25/£35
1894	1,767,635	£1	£3	£10	£35/£55

HALFPENNIES

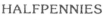

VICTORIA Old, or Widow Head · BRONZE 26mm

Date	Mintage	Peck No.	Fine	V.F.	E.F.	Unc/abt FDC
1895	3,032,154	P1950	£1	£3	£6	£15/30
1896	9,142,500	P1951	£1	£2	£5	£10/£25
1897	8,690,315	P1951A	£1	£2	£6	£12/£25
1897	Horizon higher	P1952	£2	£4	£7	£12/£20
1898	8,595,180	P1953	£1	£3	£6	£15/£20
1899	12,108,001	P1954	£1	£3	£7	£15/£25
1900	13,805,190	P1955	£1	£2	£6	£12/£16
1901	11,127,360	P1956	£1	£2	£4	£9/£12

EDWARD VII

Date	Mintage	Fine	V.F.	E.F.	Unc/abt FDC
1902	13,672,960	---	£2	£5	£10/£15
1902	LOW TIDE variety	£2	£15	£34	£60/£90
1903	11,450,880	---	£2	£9	£15/£22
1904	8,131,200	£3	£6	£12	£25/£35
1905	10,124,800	---	£1	£5	£22/£30
1906	11,101,440	---	£1	£4	£12/£20
1907	16,849,280	---	£1	£4	£12/£25
1908	16,620,800	---	£1	£5	£20/£28
1909	8,279,040	---	£4	£12	£20/£30
1910	10,769,920	---	£1	£8	£15/£20

Proofs exist for 1902; they are very rare.

"LOW TIDE" VARIETY referred to above and on page 17 may be determined thus: if the horizon meets Britannia at the point, below the knee, where right and left legs cross; NORMAL tide is indicated. If, however, the horizon meets Britannia at a much lower point - nearer the hem of her drape - then a LOW TIDE variety has been detected.

GEORGE V BRITANNIA REVERSE · BRONZE 26mm

Date	Mintage	Fine	V.F.	E.F.	abt Unc/FDC
1911	12,570,880	*Obv. 1a ---	£2	£4	£10/£15
1911	*Obverse 1b	---	£3	£6	£12/£20
1912	21,185,920	---	£2	£4	£12/£20
1913	17,476,480	---	£2	£5	£18/£25
1914	20,289,111	---	£2	£4	£12/£20
1915	21,563,040	---	£3	£6	£15/£25
1916	39,386,143	---	£1	£4	£12/£20
1917	38,245,436	---	£1	£4	£12/£20
1918	22,321,072	---	£1	£4	£12/£20
1919	28,104,001	---	£1	£4	£12/£20
1920	35,146,793	---	£1	£3	£12/£20
1920	Trial in nickel (noted 1998)	"Superb Mint State" £375			
1921	28,027,293	---	£1	£3	£10/£15
1922	10,734,964	---	£2	£5	£12/£20
1923	12,266,282	---	£1	£4	£12/£20
1924	13,971,038	---	£1	£4	£12/£20
1925	12,216,123	Head as for 1924 £1	£5	£15/£25	
1925	Modified Head	as for 1926 £3	£8	£12/£20	
1926	6,712,306	---	£2	£6	£10/£15
1927	15,589,622	---	£1	£4	£10/£15
1928	20,935,200	SMALLER HEAD: £1	£2	£6/£15	
1928	Proof	---	(noted 1988)		---/£175
1929	25,680,000	---	£1	£5	£10/£15
1930	12,532,800	---	£1	£2	£6/£12
1931	16,137,600	---	£1	£2	£6/£9
1932	14,448,000	---	£1	£2	£5/£8
1933	10,560,000	---	£1	£2	£5/£8
1934	7,704,000	---	£1	£5	£10/£15
1935	12,180,000	---	£1	£2	£5/£9
1935	(noted 1995) (P2321)	Bronze proof	"F.D.C."		£150
1936	23,008,800	---	£1	£2	£4/£6

Proofs 1926 to 1936 inclusive: British Museum.

1911	* Obverse 1a has a hollow neck · Obverse 1b has a flat neck
1911/12	Some dies were punched with date close to line of exergue
	Small gap = Rev A Clear gap = Rev B
	Combinations: 1a + A · 1a + B 1b + A · 1b + B
1925/27	Effigy modified to aid striking of all coins
1928	Smaller head adopted for halfpennies and pennies

EDWARD VIII *(Duke of Windsor)*

Date	Mintage	Fine	V.F.	E.F.	Unc/abt. FDC GOLDEN HIND
1937	Excessively rare	"Guesstimate"		£10,000 / £15,000	✗

GEORGE VI   Reverse GOLDEN HIND · BRONZE 25mm

Date	Mintage	Fine	V.F.	E.F.	Unc/abt. FDC
1937	24,504,000	---	---	50p	£1/£3
1937	26,402 proofs	---		---	£3/£5
1938	40,320,000	---	10p	£1	£2/£4
1939	28,924,800	---	10p	£1	£3/£5
1940	32,162,400	---	---	30p	£2	£4/£6
1940	Thinner rim, shorter teeth	Freeman 435			£5/£10
1941	45,120,000	---	5p	50p	£1/£3
1942	17,908,800	---	5p	50p	£1/£3
1943	76,200,000	---	10p	50p	£1/£3
1944	81,840,000	---	5p	£1	£2/£4
1945	57,000,000	---	5p	£1	£2/£4
1946	22,725,600	---	30p	£2	£4/£6
1947	21,266,400	---	10p	£1	£2/£4
1948	26,947,200	---	10p	50p	£1/£2
1949	24,744,000	---	10p	£1	£4/£6
1950	24,153,600	---	10p	£2	£6/£9
1950	17,513 proofs	---		FDC	£9
1951	14,868,000	---	20p	£2	£4/£6
1951	20,000 proofs	---		FDC	£5
1952	33,278,400	---	10p	50p	£2/£4

Proofs of all dates. Those not listed above · £150/£175

ELIZABETH II

Date	Mintage	Fine	V.F.	E.F.	abt. Unc/FDC/FDC
1953	8,910,000 :				
1953	Obverse 1	---	---	---	£3/£5
1953	Obverse 2	---	10p	20p	£1/£2
1953	40,000 proofs	---		---	£3/£6
1954	19,375,200	---	10p	£1	£3/£4/£6
1955	18,465,600	---	10p	£1	£2/£3/£5
1956	21,799,200	---	---	£1	£3/£4/£6
1957	39,672,000	---	---	20p	£1/£2/£3
1957	Variety has a calm sea	£1	£2		£4/£8/£12
1958	66,331,200	---	---	---	50p/£1/£2
1958	Proof (noted 1999)	---		---	---/£150
1959	79,176,000	---	---	---	50p/£1/£2
1960	41,340,000	---	---	---	50p/£1/£2
1961	Decimal Patterns see page 47	---			---
1962	41,779,200	---	---	---	15p/50p/£2
1963	42,720,000	---	---	---	15p/40p/£2
1964	78,583,200	---	---	---	15p/30p/£1
1965	98,083,200	---	---	---	15p/30p/£1
1965	Proofs struck in gold	---		---	£1,250
1965	Error New Zealand reverse	---		---	£450
1966	95,289,600	---	---	---	5p/15p/50p
1966	Struck in nickel-brass	---		---	£350
1966	Struck in aluminium	---		---	£250
1967	146,490,400 Narrow rim		---		5p/15p/50p
1967	(KB Coins '94) Wide rim "BU"				£2.50
	Total for 1967 includes 46,226,400 struck in 1968				
1970	750,424 LAST STERLING:				
	Proofs (1971/75)			£1/£2/£3	

Proofs of all dates. Those not listed above · £125/£145

	1940
★ ★ ★ L P ★	= Rev A
★ L ★ P ★	= Rev B
★ L	= Rev C

See 'pointings'
page 7

1949	IND:IMP (Emperor of India) discontinued · all coins
1954	BRITT:OMN discontinued · all coins
1969	Halfpenny demonetized · 1st August

Cross points BETWEEN rim beads	★ ★ +	= Obverse 1
Cross points TO a rim bead	★ ★ ★ +	= Obverse 2

Date	Mintage	Rev.	Peck No.	Fine	V.F.	E.F.	abt. Unc/FDC

GEORGE IV

ROYAL (Tower) MINT · DATE BELOW HEAD · COPPER 34mm

Date	Mintage	Rev.	Peck No.	Fine	V.F.	E.F.	abt. Unc/FDC
1825	1,075,200	A	P1420	£12	£25	£75	£200/£250
1825	Proofs	A	P1421	- - -	- - -	- - -	£200/£300
1826	5,913,000	A	P1422	£8	£20	£60	£150/£225
1826	Bronsed proof	A	P1423	- - -	- - -	- - -	£150/£200
1826	Copper proof	A	P1424	- - -	- - -	- - -	£150/£200
1826	Currency	B	P1425	£12	£20	£60	£125/£170
1826	Bronzed proof	B	P1426	- - -	- - -	- - -	£150/£200
1826	Currency	C	P1427	£15	£30	£120	£200/£300
1826	Bronzed proof	C	P1428	- - -	- - -	- - -	£200/£275
1826	Copper proof	C	P1429	- - -	- - -	- - -	£300/£450
1827	1,451,520	A	P1430				
1827	A Ext. rare		Fair £20	£100	£250	£1250	£2500/£4000
1827	A (noted 1991)		"no corrosion"	"gd.VF"	£290	- - - - -/- - - - -

WILLIAM IV

ROYAL (Tower) MINT · DATE BELOW HEAD · COPPER 34mm

Date	Mintage		Peck	Fine	V.F.	E.F.	abt. Unc/FDC
1831	806,400 no WW		P1455	£12	£45	£100	£350/£425
1831	(noted 1999)			"superb EF"	£110		- - - -/- - - -
1831	Bronzed proofs			- - -	- - -	- - -	£200/£250
1831	.W.W Incuse Initials on truncation				£60	£175	£400/£500
1831	W.W Incuse Initials		P1458★	£20	£80	£225	£450/£600
1834	322,560		P1459	£15	£50	£130	£260/£400
1837	174,720		P1460	£40	£95	£225	£500/£600

Saltire/St. Andrew's Cross varieties :

A · No central line along arms of saltire

B · Thin raised line along saltire

C · Thick/broad raised line

Date	Mintage	Peck	Fine	V.F.	E.F.	Unc/abtFDC

VICTORIA — Young Head · DATE BELOW HEAD 34mm

Date	Mintage	Peck	Fine	V.F.	E.F.	Unc/abtFDC
1839	Bronzed proof	1479	DEF : o.t.		£150	£300/£450
1841	913,920 REG:	1480	£5	£10	£30	£60/£90
1841	Proofs		- - -	- - -	- - -	£250/£400
1841	Proof in silver		(1980 "As Struck")			£1,500
1841	No colon REG	1484	£5	£10	£30	£60/£90
1841	No colon (noted 2001)		"gdE.F."	£40		- - -/- - -
1843	483,830 REG:	1486	£25	£95	£350	£700/- - - -
1843	No colon REG	1485	£30	£100	£400	£800/- - - -
1844	215,040	1487	£8	£12	£40	£80/£120
1845	322,560	1489	£9	£20	£75	£150/£225
1846	483,840 DEF :	1490	£8	£15	£50	£100/£150
1846	DEF:	1491	£8	£16	£65	£125/£175
1847	430,080 DEF:	1492	£5	£12	£45	£95/£130
1847	DEF :	1493	£5	£12	£45	£95/£130
1848	161,280	1496	£3	£10	£45	£95/£130
1848	8 over 6	1494	- -	£25	£75	£150/£225
1848	8 over 7	1495	- -	£12	£40	£80/£120
1849	268,800	1497	£40	£125	£500	£1000/£1500
1851	432,224 DEF :	1498	£6	£15	£50	£90/£125
1851	DEF:	1499	£8	£20	£60	£120/£165
1853	1,021,440 DEF :	1500	£4	£9	£25	£50/£80
1853	Narrow date		- - -	- - -	£12	£20/£40
1853	Proofs - copper and bronzed		- - -	- - -		£250/£500
1853	(noted 2001)		Bronzed proof	"nr.FDC".		£250
1853	DEF:	1503	£3	£8	£30	£75/£110
1853	Plain trident	1504	£3	£12	£30	£60/£90

VICTORIA — Young Head · DATE BELOW HEAD 34mm

Date	Mintage	Peck	Fine	V.F.	E.F.	Unc/abtFDC
1854	4 over 3	1505	£15	£45	£95	£135/£225
1854	6,720,000 p.t.	1506	£1	£6	£20	£40/£85
1854	Ornam trident	1507	£1	£6	£20	£40/£80
1854	(noted 1999)		"FDC full lustre exceptional"			£95
1855	5,273,866 o.t.	1508	£1	£7	£20	£40/£65
1855	Plain trident	1509	£1	£6	£20	£40/£60
1856	1,212,288 DEF:	p.t.	£12	£42	£150	£300/£400
1856	Plain trident proof		- - -	- - -	- - -	£250/£500
1856	DEF :	o.t.	£7	£35	£95	£250/£350
1857	752,640 DEF:	p.t.	£2	£6	£25	£50/£75
1857	DEF :	o.t.	£3	£8	£30	£60/£90
1857	Smaller date	p.t.	£2	£6	£25	£50/£75
1858	1,559,040:					
	8 over 3	1515	- -	£22	£60	£120/- - -
	8 over 6		- -	- - -	£60	- - -
	8 over 7	1516	- -	£6	£25	£50/£75
	Smaller date	1517	£1	£6	£25	£50/£75
	Large date no W.W.	1518	£1	£5	£20	£40/£60
1859	1,075,200 Large date		£3	£8	£30	£60/£90
1859	9 over 8		£4	£16	£42	£95/£130
1859	Smaller date		£3	£9	£35	£80/£125
1859	Proof		- - -	- - -	- - -	£500/£750
1860	60 struck over 59		£150	£400	£950	- - - -/- - -
1860	60 struck over 59 ↓Rev.			£500	£950	- - - -/£1500

NEAR COLON:

FAR COLON :

DEF: = near colon - DEF: = far colon - o.t. = ornamental trident
plain tridents have near colons   p.t. = plain trident
All have ornamental tridents from 1839 to 1851

BRONZE · DATE BELOW BRITANNIA · 31mm

Rev	Peck		F.	V.F.	E.F.	Abt. Unc.
1860	5,053,440	TYPE 1		BEADED RIM BORDER		
		Obverse: L.C.WYON ON TRUNCATION				
A	1617		£3	£15	£35	£80
B	1619		£6	£30	£70	£160
B	1620	extra heavy flan	- - -	£750	- - - -	- - - -
B	1620A	proof in gold (noted 1997)		- - - -		£15,000
B	1621	silver proof	- -	- - -	- - - -	(£500 EF+)
B	1622	bronzed proof	- -	- - -	- - - -	£500
C	1623		£10	£45	£95	- - -
Mule	1624	bead obv/tooth rev	£95	£250	£500	
Mule	1628	tooth obv/bead rev	£250	£600	£1200	✳

		TYPE 2		TOOTHED RIM/BORDER		
		Obverse: L.C.WYON ON or BELOW TRUNCATION				
C★	1625	signature on	£9	£35	£70	
C★		(S & B 1995) "gdEF much lustre"	£45	- - -		
D	1626	signature on	£25	£95	£225	
C★	1629	signature on	- - -	£35	£70	
C★	1630	struck on heavy flan	£250	- - -		
C★	1631	bronze proof	- - -	£250		
C★	1632	signature below	£10	£40	£75	
C★	1633	no sig. 15 leaves	£50	£90	- - -	
C★	1635	no sig. 16 leaves	£50	£90	- - -	
	1634	ONF PENNY variety: damaged die				
			£12	£45	£175	£375/- - - -
	2051	Wyon Pattern MDCCCLX · nickel alloy :				
		(Seaby 1989) "gdEF" £450		- - - -/- - - -		

The design is described, in exquisite detail, by Michael J. Freeman in his book "The Bronze Coinage of Great Britain".

1860 reverse: L.C.W. incuse below shield
Rev. A = crosses outlined with treble incuse lines, Britannia's thumb touches cross of St. George, no rock to left of lighthouse.
Rev. B = crosses outlined by close, double, raised lines, Britannia's thumb does not touch cross, no rock to left of lighthouse.
Rev. C = similar to Rev. B, but lines thinner and wider apart, small rock to left of lighthouse.
Rev. C★ = as Rev. C, but with minor modifications to rocks and sea and, of course, a toothed border.
Rev. D = as Rev. C, but L.C.W. incuse below foot.

Peck/Freeman comparisons	
Peck 'A'	= Freeman 'B'
Peck 'B'	= Freeman 'A'
Peck 'C'	= Freeman 'C'
Peck 'C★'	= Freeman 'D'
Peck 'D'	= Freeman 'E'

Rev	Peck		F.	V.F.	E.F.	abt. UNC/FDC

1861 36,449,280 Obverse: L.C.WYON ON or BELOW TRUNCATION

Rev	Peck		F.	V.F.	E.F.	abt. UNC/FDC
C★	1637	signature on	- - -	£120	- - -	- - -
F	1638	no signature	£20	£75	- - -	- - -
C★	1639	sig. below	£5	£12	£30	£60/£80
F	1642	no signature	£20	£75	- - -	- - -
C★	1643	no sig 15 leaves	£35	- - -	- - -	- - -
C★	1644	no sig 16 leaves	£5	£12	£30	£60/£80
		6 over 8 Fair £50	£95	£225	- - -	- - -
F	1646	no sig	£5	£12	£30	£60/£80

OBVERSE 5 · No Signature · Wreath of 16 leaves · Raised midribs
REVERSE F · No signature · Thumb does not touch St.George's cross

Date	Mintage		F.	V.F.	E.F.	abt. UNC/FDC
1862	50,534,400		£1	£5	£25	£40/£60
1862	Bronzed proof		- - -	- - -	- - -	£400
1862	Date from halfpenny die (smaller):					
	Fair £60	£95	£250	- - -		- - - -
1862	8 over 6		"gdVF"	£275		(Seaby 1989)
1862	Pattern cu-nickel P2060			"FDC"		£600
1863	28,062,720 (P1655)		£1	£8	£30	£60/£80
1863	Bronzed proof		- - -	- - -	- - -	£250
1863	Die number below date:					
	2 below		£300	- - -		(noted 1996)
	3 below Fair £100		- - -	- - -		(noted 1988)
	4 below		£250	- - -		(noted 1998)
1864	3,440,646 Plain 4		£15	£50	£200	£350/£450
1864	Crosslet 4		£20	£75	£250	£425/£525
1865	8,601,600		£2	£9	£45	£90/- - - -
1865	5 over 3		£30	£75	£175	£400/£750
1865	Pattern P2061		- - -	- - -	"nrFDC"	£300
1866	9,999,360		£3	£10	£30	£60/- - - -
1867	5,483,520		£4	£15	£40	£90/- - - -
1867	Proof in silver (noted 2000)		- - -		"abt.FDC"	£667
1868	1,182,720		£6	£20	£75	£150/- - - -
1868	Bronze proof P1681			(noted 1998)		£425
1868	Copper-nickel proof		- -	- - -	£250	£400
1869	2,580,480		£30	£95	£325	£650/- - - -
1870	5,695,022		£5	£15	£75	£150/- - - -
1871	1,290,318		£15	£60	£200	£325/- - - -
1872	8,494,572		£3	£12	£30	£75/- - - -
1873	8,494,200		£3	£12	£30	£60/£80

O/R	Peck		F.	V.F.	E.F.	abt. abt. UNC/FDC

OBVERSE 5; and OBVERSE 6 (a MORE MATRONLY PORTRAIT)
REVERSE F; and REVERSE G (a LESS GRACEFUL BRITANNIA)

1874   5,621,86 :

O/R	Peck		F.	V.F.	E.F.	abt. abt. UNC/FDC
5/F	1690		£5	£15	£50	£100/£150
5/G	1691		£10	£30	£60	- - - -/- - - -
6/F	1692		£5	£15	£50	£100/£150
6/G	1693		£10	£30	£60	- - - -/- - - -

1874H 6,666,240 : 'H' centrally, in exergue, below date indicates coins struck at Heaton Mint

O/R	Peck		F.	V.F.	E.F.	abt. abt. UNC/FDC
5/F	1694		£5	£15	£50	£100/£175
5/G	1695		£10	£25	£60	- - -/- - - -
6/F	1696		£5	£15	£50	£90/- - - -
6/G	1697		£5	£15	£50	£85/- - - -
6/G	1698	Bronze proof	- -	- - -	- - -	£350

Rev. E = no signature, thumb touches St. George's Cross; no vertical lines to lantern
Rev. F = no signature, thumb does not touch Cross, lantern has six vertical lines
Rev. G = Britannia has long, thin neck; her helmet is tall and narrow; a tall, thin lighthouse

VICTORIA   "Bun" Head   (continued)

Date	Mintage	F.	V.F.	E.F.	Abt. Unc/FDC
1875	10,691,040	£2	£7	£25	£50/£75
1875H	752,640	£25	£80	£200	£400/----
1875H	Proof P1706 (noted 2001)			"FDC"	£500
1876H	11,074,560	£3	£9	£30	£60/---
1877	Narrow date £200	---	---	---	---/---
1877	9,624,747	£2	£7	£25	£40/£75
1877	Proof cupro-nickel	---	"nr.FDC"		---/£700
1878	2,764,470	£3	£10	£40	£80/£120
1878	Proof P1713	---	"nr.FDC"		---/£275
1879	7,666,476	£2	£6	£24	£40/£55
1879	Narrow date	£10	£20	£60	£120/---
1879	Re-touched Obv. P1715		£75	"gdEF"	
1880	3,000,831	£3	£10	£40	£80/£120
1880	Proof (noted 1999)			"abt.FDC"	---/£500
1881	2,302,261	£2	£10	£42	£65/£95
1881	Portrait 'aged' further:				
	P1722	£4	£15	£50	£75/£95
1881H	3,763,200	£2	£10	£25	£50/£75
1881H	(noted 2001) "Unc good lustre"				£70
1881H	Heraldically coloured shield				£50/---
1882H	7,526,400	£2	£6	£20	£40/£60
1882	No H (beware removal)			£600	£900/----
1883	6,237,438	£2	£7	£25	£45/£70
1884	11,702,802	£2	£5	£20	£40/£60
1885	7,145,862	£2	£5	£20	£35/£55
1886	6,087,759	£2	£4	£15	£30/£45
1887	5,315,085	£1	£4	£15	£30/£45
1887	Aluminium pattern (P2175)		(1999)		£400
1888	5,125,020	£1	£4	£15	£30/£45
1889	12,559,737	£1	£4	£14	£26/£40
1889	Narrow date (P1745)		£25		---/---
1890	15,330,840	£1	£4	£15	£30/£45
1891	17,885,961	£1	£4	£15	£35/£50
1892	10,501,671	£1	£4	£15	£30/£45
1893	8,161,737	£1	£5	£16	£32/£48
1894	3,883,452	£3	£12	£30	£60/£80

Proofs for 1881, 1884/85/86 and 1890/91/92
All proofs except, perhaps, 1888 £400/£500

VICTORIA Old, Veiled, or Widow Head

Date	Mintage	F.	V.F.	E.F.	Abt. Unc/FDC
1895	5,395,830 Rev B		£4	£8	£18/£30
1895	No sea Rev A	£10	£30	£80	£175/£250
1895	Pattern (P2066) (noted 1999)				---/£800
1896	24,147,156	£1	£3	£8	£16/£30
1896	9 and 6 further apart	£5	£10	£25/£40	
1897	20,756,620	£1	£3	£6	£12/£20
1897	Higher horizon		---	£100	£200
1898	14,296,836	£1	£3	£10	£20/£30
1899	26,441,069	£1	£4	£8	£18/£36
1900	31,778,109	---	£1	£4	£8/£16
1900	Proofs	---	---	"FDC"	£300
1901	22,205,568	---	£1	£5	£10/£15
1901	Proofs	---	---	"FDC"	£300

1895	Rev A, trident to P is 2mm; no sea behind
1895	Rev B, trident to P is 1mm; sea behind (to left of) Britannia

EDWARD VII — BRONZE 31mm

Date	Mintage	Fine	V.F.	E.F.	abt. Unc/FDC
1902	26,976,768	30p	£3	£5	£12/£20
1902	LOW TIDE variety	£3	£10	£25	£40/£60
1903	21,415,296	---	£4	£10	£20/£30
1903	Open '3'	£15	£25	£60	---/---
1904	12,913,152	---	£5	£15	£25/£35
1905	17,783,808	---	£4	£12	£20/£30
1906	37,989,504	---	£4	£8	£15/£25
1907	47,322,240	---	£3	£9	£18/£24
1908	31,506,048	---	£3	£10	£20/£30
1908	(Coincraft 1998) lists a matt proof on thick flan				£1,000
1909	19,617,024	---	£3	£9	£18/£24
1910	29,549,184	---	£4	£10	£20/£30

GEORGE V — BRONZE 31mm

Date	Mintage	Fine	V.F.	E.F.	abt. Unc/FDC
1911	23,079,168	(1 + A)	£4	£8	£15/£22
1911	Hollow neck	(see page 6)	(1988 GEF £20)		
1912	48,306,048	(1 + A)	£3	£8	£15/£22
1912H	16,800,000	(1 + A)	£5	£20	£30/£45
1913	65,497,872	(2 + B)	£3	£6	£12/£20
1914	50,820,997	---	£3	£8	£15/£25
1915	47,310,807	---	£3	£5	£10/£15
1916	86,411,165	---	£2	£3	£9/£12
1917	107,905,436	---	£2	£3	£10/£15
1918	84,227,372	---	£2	£3	£9/£12
1918H	3,660,800	£1	£10	£70	£140/£200
1918H	(noted 1999) "BU full lustre"				£165/---
1918KN	Inc above	£2	£15	£95	£200/£260
1919	113,761,090	---	£1	£5	£10/£15
1919H	5,209,600	£1	£10	£70	£140/£200
1919KN	Inc above	£2	£20	£100	£250/£300
1920	124,693,485	(2 + B)	£2	£5	£10/£20
1920	(P2259)	(3 + B)	---	---	---/---
1921	129,717,693	(2 + B)	£2	£5	£12/£22
1921	(P2261)	(3 + B)	£2	£5	£12/£22
1922	16,346,711	(3 + B)	£3	£15	£30/£50
1923 to 1925 None		---	---	---	
1926	4,498,519	---	£5	£25	£50/£75
1926	Modified effigy	£3	£20	£200	£450/£650
1927	60,989,561	---	£2	£4	£6/£10

Toothed circle of rev A has 163 teeth whilst B has 188

Illustrations of H (Heaton) and KN (Kings Norton) appear on page 18

Obverse 1: bottom stop of colon close to A; GRA: BRITT
Obverse 2: stops are midway but cramped; GRA:BRITT
Obverse 3: as obverse 2 but words farther apart; GRA : BRITT :

1913 1+A rarer than 2+B
rarer still are 2+A and 1+B

GEORGE V — SMALLER HEAD · BRONZE 31mm

Date	Mintage	Fine	V.F.	E.F.	Unc/abtFDC
1928	50,178,000	---	£2	£4	£8/£12
1929	49,132,800	---	£1	£5	£7/£12
1930	29,097,600	---	£1	£6	£9/£15
1931	19,843,200	---	£1	£7	£14/£21
1932	8,277,600	---	£3	£15	£30/£45
1932	Proof (P2278) (noted 1999)			"FDC"	£300
1933	7 or 8 plus "patterns"	(Spink 1994)			£25,300
1933	Pattern by Lavrillier		(1986)		£4,100
1933	A uniface	---		(1980 £28,750)	£50,000
1934	13,965,600	---	£2	£9	£20/£30
1935	56,070,000	---	£1	£3	£4/£8
1935	Bronze proof (noted 1999)			"FDC"	£250
1936	154,296,000	---	£1	£2	£3/£5

Proofs for all dates from 1926 to 1936 except 1933

In addition to the 7, possibly 8, pennies listed at left (left-hand pair above); there were patterns, possibly four, struck from dies engraved by André Lavrillier (right-hand pair above) having a 'military' King George V, a thick trident and a sea of wavy lines. Yet another 1933 penny is uniface: having a "tail" but the "head" replaced by the word MODEL. The 1933 set from St. Mary's Church, Hawksworth Wood, was offered for sale at Sotheby's in 1972. It fetched £7,000. This set was one of those placed under foundation stones laid by King George in 1933.

PENNIES

EDWARD VIII (Duke of Windsor)

Date	Mintage	Fine	V.F.	E.F.	abt. Unc/FDC
1937	Specimen strikings only, "guesstimate" from £15,000				

GEORGE VI — BRONZE 31mm

Date	Mintage	Fine	V.F.	E.F.	abt. Unc/FDC
1937	88,896,000	---	50p	£1	£2/£4
1937	26,402 proofs	---	---	£3	£4/£8
1938	121,560,000	---	20p	£1	£2/£4
1939	55,560,000	---	60p	£2	£4/£6
1940	42,284,400	£1	£3	£6	£10/£20
1941 to 1943 none		---	---	---	---
1944	42,600,000	---	60p	£3	£6/£9
1944	not toned by Royal Mint	---	---		£8/£16
1945	79,531,200	---	50p	£2	£3/£5
1945	Doubled 9	£1	£5	£25	---
1946	66,855,600	---	30p	£2	£4/£6
1947	52,220,400	---	30p	£2	£3/£4
1948	63,961,200	---	10p	£1	£2/£3
1949	14,324,400	---	20p	£1	£2/£3
1950	240,000	£2	£6	£12	£18/£25
1950	17,513 proofs	---	---	FDC	£20
1951	120,000	£3	£8	£12	£20/£30
1951	20,000 proofs	---	---	FDC	£18

Proofs for all dates. Those not listed above, £250

1937	Rev Aa	Ns point to border teeth	•••• N N
1937	Rev Ab	Ns point between teeth (b is rarer)	•••• N N
1940	Rev Ab	has single exergue line	
1940	Rev B	has double exergue line (Ab is rarer)	
1944	Rev Ba	waves touch exergue	
1944	Rev Bb	gap between waves and exergue	

ELIZABETH II — BRONZE 31mm

Date	Mintage	Fine	V.F.	E.F.	abt. Unc/FDC
1953	Pattern (not in Peck) unique ? : has toothed (not beaded) border			Spink	£1,950
1953	1,308,400 (from the 'Plastic' Set)			£1	£2/£4
1953	(noted 1999)	---	"BU. Full lustre"		£5
1953	40,000 proofs	---	---		£6/£9
1953	Pattern from sand-blasted dies	---	---		£250
1954	1 retrieved from change. Now in British Museum.				
1954	It is believed there are others		"guesstimate"		£24,000
1955 to 1960 none		---	---	---	---
1961	48,313,400	---	---	---	25p/60p
1962	157,588,600	---	---	---	20p/50p
1963	119,733,600	---	---	---	---/25p
1964	153,294,000	---	---	---	12p/50p
1965	121,310,400	---	---	---	15p/50p
1965	In gold, unofficial, (Christies 1989 £1300)				£2500
1966	165,739,200	---	---	---	---/25p
1966	2 (so far) Jersey penny obverse. (Auction 1992)				£605
1967	155,280,000	---	---	---	---/15p
1968	170,400,000 all dated 1967				
1969	219,360,000 all dated 1967				
1970	109,524,000 all dated 1967:		654,564,000		

Proofs for some dates. 1970 proofs from the sets   £2   £3/£4

For a coin valued/costing less than £1, it should be borne in mind that almost ALL the value/cost lies in the handling, listing and storing of that coin. Whilst it enables collections to be expanded; such a small sum, even multiplied by many coins, is unlikely to be recoverable by re-selling. A long life, however, could make all the difference and we wish you exactly that!

H-Heaton Mint Mark

KN-Kings Norton Mint Mark

THREE HALFPENCES

ISSUED FOR COLONIAL USE

Date	Mintage	Fine	V.F.	E.F.	abt. Unc/FDC
WILLIAM IV					SILVER 12mm
1834	800,448	£5	£10	£30	£50/£60
1835	633,600	£10	£20	£50	£90/£120
1835	5 struck over 4	£6	£12	£30	£55/£75
1836	158,400	£3	£12	£25	£40/£60
1837	30,624	£10	£25	£90	£150/£180

Date	Mintage	Fine	V.F.	E.F.	abt. Unc/FDC
VICTORIA					SILVER 12mm
1838	538,560	£3	£9	£20	£30/£45
1839	760,320	£2	£8	£18	£25/£40
1840	95,040	£7	£20	£50	£90/£125
1841	158,400	£4	£10	£25	£50/£65
1842	1,869,120	£4	£10	£25	£50/£65
1843	475,200	£1	£4	£12	£25/£40
1843	43 over 34	£5	£18	£40	£60/£90
1843	43 over 34	Proof	- - -	- - -	£500
1860	160,000	£2	£10	£35	£65/£95
1862	256,000	£2	£10	£30	£60/£90
1862	Proof	(Seaby 1990)		abt.FDC	£475
1870	Proof, or pattern	(1986)	- - -		£325
1870	Proof, or pattern	(1996)	- - -		£750
1870	Proof, or pattern	(1999)	- - -		£950
1870	Proof, or pattern	(2000)	- - -		£950

THREEPENCES

Date	Mintage	Fine	V.F.	E.F.	abt. Unc/FDC
GEORGE IV					SILVER 16mm
1822	small head (from Maundy 2d)	£3	£12	£25	£40/£50
1822	from Maundy proof set	- - -	- - -	- - -	- - -/- - -
1823	larger 'normal' head	£1	£6	£12	£24/£36
1824		£1	£6	£12	£24/£36
1825		£1	£6	£12	£24/£36
1826		£2	£10	£30	£50/£75
1826	(noted 1999)	- -	"gdEF"	£35	- - -/- - -
1827		£1	£6	£12	£24/£36
1828		£1	£6	£12	£24/£36
1828	from Maundy proof set	- - -	- - -	- - -	- - -/- - -
1829		£3	£9	£18	£36/£45
1830		£2	£8	£16	£30/£40

Date	Mintage	Fine	V.F.	E.F.	abt. Unc/FDC
WILLIAM IV					SILVER 16mm
1831	from Maundy set	£1	£10	£20	£30/£50
1831	from proof set	- -	- - -	- - -	£50/£65
1832	from Maundy set	£1	£10	£20	£21/£36
1833	from Maundy set	£1	£10	£20	£21/£36
For use in West Indies - unpolished surface:					
1834	401,016	£3	£15	£35	£70/£100
1835	491,040	£3	£15	£30	£65/£95
1836	411,840	£3	£15	£35	£70/£90
1837	42,768	£5	£20	£45	£90/£125

VICTORIA — Young Head (as Maundy but 'dull' surface)

Date	Mintage	Fine	V.F.	E.F.	abt. Unc/FDC.
1838	1,203,840	£3	£8	£40	£60/£90
1838	BRITANNIAB	extremely rare	- - - -		- - -/- - -
1839	570,240	£3	£9	£45	£90/£120
1839	Proof (from proof Maundy Set)	- - -			£200
1840	633,600	£3	£9	£45	£90/£120
1841	443,520	£4	£10	£45	£90/£120
1842	2,027,520	£4	£10	£45	£90/£120
1843	Included above	£2	£6	£30	£60/£95
1844	1,045,400	£2	£8	£40	£80/£110

Preceding coins were for use only in the colonies.

Date	Mintage	Fine	V.F.	E.F.	abt. Unc/FDC.
1845	1,314,720	£3	£9	£25	£50/£70
1846	47,520	£15	£30	£120	£250/- - -
1847	(Spink 2000)	- -	- - -	£350	- - -/- - -
1848	(Spink 2000)	£40	£125	£325	- - -/- - -
1849	126,720	£4	£12	£50	£75/£100
1850	950,400	£4	£10	£25	£50/£80
1851	479,065	£4	£10	£30	£60/£100
1851	5 struck over 8	£8	£20	£60	£120/£200
1852	(Coincraft Cat '95)	£50	£100	£250	- - -/- - -
1853	31,680	£15	£30	£120	£200/- - -
1854	1,467,246	£4	£8	£30	£50/£75
1855	383,350	£4	£9	£35	£80/- - -
1856	1,013,760	£4	£9	£35	£80/- - -
1857	1,758,240	£4	£9	£35	£80/- - -
1858	1,441,440	£4	£8	£35	£70/£95
1858	BRITANNIAB	£30	£120	£250	- - -/- - -
1859	3,579,840	£3	£6	£25	£40/£60
1860	3,405,600	£4	£9	£35	£60/£95
1861	3,294,720	£3	£6	£25	£45/£70
1862	1,156,320	£3	£8	£30	£60/£90
1863	950,400	£3	£8	£30	£65/£95
1864	1,330,560	£3	£6	£25	£40/£60
1865	1,742,400	£3	£8	£35	£70/£95
1866	1,900,800	£3	£6	£25	£40/£60
1867	712,800	£3	£7	£30	£50/£75
1868	1,457,280	£3	£6	£25	£40/£60
1868	RRITANNIAR	£20	£60	£200	- - -/- - -
1868	Laureate Head pattern by Wyon		- - -		- - -/- - -
1869	4,488 Maundy	£6	£12	£55	£95/- - -

VICTORIA — Young Head (SILVER 16mm)

Date	Mintage	Fair/Fine	V.F.	E.F.	abt. Unc/FDC
1870	1,283,218	£1/£3	£6	£25	£35/£60
1871	999,633	£1/£3	£6	£30	£45/£70
1872	1,293,271	£1/£3	£6	£30	£45/£70
1873	4,055,550	£1/£3	£5	£15	£30/£45
1874	4,427,031	£1/£3	£5	£15	£30/£45
1875	3,306,500	£1/£3	£5	£15	£30/£45
1876	1,834,389	£1/£3	£5	£15	£30/£45
1877	2,622,393	£1/£3	£5	£15	£30/£45
1878	2,419,975	£1/£3	£5	£15	£30/£45
1879	3,140,265	£1/£3	£5	£15	£30/£45
1880	1,610,069	£1/£3	£6	£18	£35/£50
1881	3,248,265	£1/£3	£6	£18	£35/£50
1882	472,965	£1/£4	£15	£25	£45/£70
1883	4,365,971	£1/£3	£5	£15	£30/£45
1884	3,322,424	£1/£3	£5	£15	£30/£45
1885	5,183,653	£1/£3	£5	£15	£30/£45
1886	6,152,669	£1/£3	£5	£15	£30/£45
1887	2,780,761 YOUNG	£1/£3	£5	£15	£30/£45
	Young Head proof		- - -	- - -	£200/- -

Jubilee Head

Date	Mintage	Fair/Fine	V.F.	E.F.	abt. Unc/FDC
1887	Included above	£2	£4	£6	£8/£12
1887	Jubilee Head proof	- - -	- - -		£35/£45
1888	518,199	£2	£4	£8	£15/£25
1889	4,587,010	£2	£4	£6	£12/£20
1890	4,465,834	£2	£4	£6	£12/£20
1891	6,323,027	£2	£4	£6	£12/£20
1892	2,578,226	£2	£4	£6	£12/£20
1893	3,067,243 JUBILEE	£8	£25	£75	£125/£175

Old or Widow Head

Date	Mintage	Fair/Fine	V.F.	E.F.	abt. Unc/FDC
1893	Included above	£2	£4	£6	£12/£18
1893	1,312 Proofs	- -	- - -	- - -	£30/£40
1893	(noted 1999)	- -	- - -	"FDC"	£45
1894	1,608,603	£3	£5	£8	£15/£20
1895	4,788,609	£3	£5	£8	£15/£20
1896	4,598,442	£3	£5	£8	£15/£20
1897	4,541,294	£2	£4	£6	£12/£18
1898	4,567,177	£2	£4	£6	£12/£18
1899	6,246,281	£2	£4	£6	£12/£18
1900	10,644,480	£2	£4	£6	£12/£18
1901	6,098,400	£1	£3	£5	£10/£15

★ Threepences bearing dates not listed are, probably, Maundy pieces.

EDWARD VII

Date	Mintage	Fine	V.F.	E.F.	abt. Unc/FDC
					SILVER 16mm
1902	8,268,480	£1	£2	£5	£10/- -
1902	15,123 proofs		- - -		£10/£15
1903	5,227,200	£2	£6	£22	£40/£50
1904	3,627,360	£3	£8	£25	£40/£60
1905	3,548,160	£3	£8	£20	£35/£45
1906	3,152,160	£2	£8	£20	£35/£45
1907	4,831,200	£1	£3	£9	£15/£25
1908	8,157,600	£2	£4	£12	£20/£30
1909	4,055,040	£2	£4	£12	£20/£30
1910	4,563,380	£1	£3	£9	£15/£25

GEORGE V   SILVER (.925 to 1920 then .500) 16mm

Date	Mintage	Fine	V.F.	E.F.	abt. Unc/FDC
1911	5,841,084	75p	£2	£4	£9/£15
1911	6,001 proofs		- - -	- - -	£20
1912	8,932,825	60p	£1	£3	£8/£14
1913	7,143,242	60p	£1	£3	£8/£14
1914	6,733,584	60p	£1	£3	£8/£14
1915	5,450,617	60p	£2	£4	£8/£15
1916	18,555,201	60p	£1	£3	£6/£9
1917	21,662,490	60p	£1	£2	£4/£6
1918	20,630,909	60p	£1	£2	£4/£6
1919	16,845,687	60p	£1	£2	£4/£6
1920	16,703,597	50p	£1	£2	£4/£6
1920	.500 silver	50p	£1	£3	£7/£12
1921	8,749,301	50p	£1	£3	
1922	7,979,998	50p	£1	£6	£12/£20
1923	Small number of patterns, struck in nickel				
1923	Trial with "MODEL" obv. (auc. 2000) £460				
1925	3,731,859	£1	£2	£6	£12/£18
1925	Patterns, in nickel, of new (1927) design				- -
1926	4,107,910	£1	£3	£12	£25/£32
1926 Modified Effigy		50p	£1	£5	£18/£25

1904	Large '3' closer to bow at bottom and crown at top.
1911	{ Obv. 1a = neck hollow } as described on page 6. { Obv. 1b = neck flat }

GEORGE V   SILVER (50%) 16mm

Date	Mintage	Fine	V.F.	E.F.	abt. Unc/FDC
1927	15,022 proofs oak sprig/acorn reverse				£25/£35
1928	1,302,106	75p	£2	£10	£20/£30
1929	None	- - -	- - -	- - -	- - -/- - -
1930	1,319,412	50p	£1	£10	£20/£30
1930	(noted 1999)	- - -	- - -	"FDC"	- - -/£22
1931	6,251,936	50p	£1	£2	£3/£4
1932	5,887,325	50p	£1	£2	£3/£4
1933	5,578,541	50p	£1	£2	£3/£4
1934	7,405,954	50p	£1	£2	£4/£6
1934	A proof offered for sale in 1976 (!)				/£55
1934	Proof (listed in Coincraft Cat. 1997)				£250
1935	7,027,654	25p	50p	£1	£3/£4
1936	3,238,670	25p	50p	£1	£2/£3

EDWARD VIII   (Duke of Windsor)

1937	Pattern bearing a design of three rings "guesstimate" £9500/£12000
1937	Silver 'thrift plant' proof by Maklouf "FDC" £20
1937	Silver 'ER monogram' proof by Maklouf "FDC" £16

GEORGE VI   SILVER (50%) 16mm

Date	Mintage	Fine	V.F.	E.F.	abt. Unc/FDC
1937	8,148,156	25p	50p	£1	£2/£3
1937	26,402 proofs	- - -	- - -	- - -	£3/£5
1938	6,402,473	25p	50p	£2	£4/£6
1939	1,355,860	25p	50p	£3	£6/£9
1940	7,914,401	25p	50p	£1	£2/£3
1941	7,979,411	25p	50p	£1	£2/£3
1942	4,144,051 Colonial	£1	£2	£5	£9/£15
1943	1,379,220 Colonial	£2	£3	£6	£12/£20
1944	2,005,553 Colonial	£3	£7	£12	£24/£35
1945	371,000 dated 1944; re-melted by The Mint
1945	An "Escapee" (Coincraft '97 VF £4,000)

ELIZABETH II

Date	Mintage	Fine	V.F.	E.F.	abt. Unc/FDC
1953	Maundy Silver 3d	- -	£25	£30	£60/- - -
1954 to 1970		- -	£8	£12	£15/- - -
1970 to 1997		- -	- -	£12	£15/- - -

Date	Mintage	Fine	V.F.	E.F.	Unc/abt FDC

EDWARD VIII Duke of Windsor

1937   Date divided by THRIFT PLANT (Sea-pink); a few were made for
     slot machine testing and thicknesses vary. Spinks (1990) £28.500
                              Cooke (1994) £24.500
1937   Date at bottom, but effigy Edward VIII. Coincraft ('99) £20.000
     Lettering is EDWARDIVS VIII *not* GEORGIVS VI.

GEORGE VI   MODIFIED THRIFT PLANT

Date	Mintage	Fine	V.F.	E.F.	Unc/abt FDC
1937	45,707,957	---	50p	£1	£2/£3
1937	(Welsh 1996)	---		"Gem, BU/FDC"	--/£4
1937	26,402 proofs	---	---	£3	£6/£9
1938	14,532,332	5p	50p	£3	£6/£9
1939	5,603,021	12p	£1	£4	£15/£20
1940	12,636,018	10p	£1	£2	£4/£6
1941	60,239,489	---	£1	£2	£3/£4
1942	103,214,400	---	£1	£2	£3/£4
1943	101,702,400	---	£1	£2	£3/£4
1944	69,760,000	---	£1	£2	£3/£4
1945	33,942,466	---	£1	£3	£5/£8
1946	620,734	£1	£10	£40	£125/£200
1946	(noted 1999)	---	"gd.E.F."	£70	----/----
1946	Proof	"FDC"	(1985) £250	---	(1999) £360
1947	None	---	---	---	---
1948	4,230,400	---	£1	£5	£15/£20

IND. IMP discontinued

Date	Mintage	Fine	V.F.	E.F.	Unc/abt FDC
1949	464,000	£2	£10	£60	£120/£160
1949	A proof in brass	---	---	---	£200/£400
1950	1,600,000	10p	£3	£15	£30/£50
1950	17,513 proofs	---	---	---	£15/£25
1951	1,184,000	10p	£3	£18	£40/£60
1951	20,000 proofs	---	---	---	£25/£30
1952	25,494,400	---	£1	£2	£3/£4

     British Museum has proof/s of each date

1937   Two different spacings from rim of word THREE noted :
        Rev. A = large gap;   Rev. B = small gap

Sharp v Rounded Corners:	Tiny Initials of designers:
1937 - 1940 All sharp	H.P. = T. Humphrey Paget
1941 - Both	K.G. = Kruger Gray
1942 - 1946 All rounded	W.P. = Wilson Parker
1948 - Both	M.G. = Mary Gillick
1949 - All rounded	W.G.= William Gardner
1950 - 1952 All sharp	

ELIZABETH II
PORTCULLIS with CHAINS, ROYALLY CROWNED

Date	Mintage	Fine	V.F.	E.F.	abt. Unc/FDC
1953	30,618,000	BRITT.OMN	25p	75p	£1/£2
1953	40,000 proofs Obv.2	---	£2	£4/£6	
1954	41,720,000	no BRITT.OMN	25p	£1	£3/£5
1954	Matt proof	(1982 "Unc" £95)		(1997 "FDC" £150)	
1955	41,075,200	---	25p	£1	£2/£4
1956	36,801,600	---	45p	£2	£4/£6
1957	24,294,400	---	25p	£2	£4/£6
1958	20,504,000	---	45p	£2	£4/£8
1958	Proof	(Coincraft 1993)		"FDC"	£275
1959	28,499,200	---	---	£1	£2/£3
1960	83,078,400	---	---	50p	£1/£2
1961	41,102,400	---	---	20p	50p/£1
1962	51,545,600	---	---	20p	40p/95p
1963	35,280,000	---	---	20p	50p/£1
1964	44,867,200	---	---	10p	50p/75p
1965	27,160,000	---	---	10p	50p/75p
1966	53,760,000	---	---	10p	20p/50p
1967	151,780,800	---	---	5p	10p/25p
1970	750,476	proofs for LAST STERLING set			£2/£3

Undated error - double obverse ("heads") both sides   £350

V.A.T., not included here, is sometimes
absorbed by the seller on a 'special offer' basis.

1953 (a) = I of ELIZABETH points to corner of rim/edge.
       (b) = I is much further to the right (see page 7).

1953 Obv. 1 Details, particularly head ribbon and initials M.G. are
           poorly defined = ex-specimen set (page 55).
       Obv. 2 Portrait more sharply outlined as are the ends of
           the head ribbon = normal issue. Both have ovoid stops.
1954 Much sharper overall and with round stops.

WILLIAM IV — Reverse has FOUR PENCE in words - SILVER 16mm

Date	Mintage	Fair/Fine	V.F.	E.F.	abt. Unc./FDC
1836	Britannia seated : D :	£2/£5	£10	£20	£40/£60
1836	Colons close to :D:	£5	£20	£40	--- / ---
1836	Proofs, grained (milled) edge in silver		---	--- / £200
1836	Proofs, plain edge in gold (Coincraft Cat '99)			£4,000
1836	Proofs, plain edge in silver	---	£275	--- / £350
1836	Proof, in silver on thin flan	---	---	--- / £600
1837	962,280	£3/£6	£15	£30	£45/£65

A number of patterns exist

> The FOURPENCE, not the silver threepence, is the true "Joey": taking its name from one Joseph Hume who recommended it to facilitate payment of the, then, 4d London omnibus fare.

VICTORIA — FOUR PENCE in words - SILVER 16mm

Date	Mintage	Fair/Fine	V.F.	E.F.	abt. Unc./FDC
1837	Proof only - plain edged	---		--- / £1200
1837	Proof only - grained (milled) edge	---		--- / £1200
1838	2,150,280	£4	£8	£20	£36/£50
1838	2nd 8 struck over ∞	£10	£20	£40	£60/£95
1838	Plain edged proof	---	---	---	£150
1839	1,461,240	£1/£3	£6	£18	£36/£50
1839	Plain edged proof from the sets	↑↑	---		£150
1839	Obverse/Reverse alignment	↑↓	---		£200

VICTORIA — FOUR PENCE in words - SILVER 16mm

Date	Mintage	Fair/Fine	V.F.	E.F.	Unc/abtFDC
1840	1,496,880:				
	Large date	£3/£6	£12	£18	£36/£50
	Small date	£3/£6	£15	£25	£40/£60
1840	(Mason 1994) "1840 over O · gd.VF £12 · Unrecorded overdate"				
1841	344,520	£4	£8	£20	£40/£60
1841	Second 1 over I	£4	£8	£20	£40/£60
1842	724,680	£1/£3	£6	£12	£36/£50
1842	Plain edged proof	---	---	---	£200
1842	2 struck over 1	£5	£10	£50	-- / ----
1843	1,817,640	£2	£6	£18	£36/£54
1844	855,360	£2	£6	£20	£50/£70
1845	914,760	£2	£6	£20	£50/£65
1846	1,366,200	£1	£5	£20	£50/£65
1847	7 struck over 6	£15	£60	£240	--- / ----
1848	712,800	£5	£10	£20	£40/£60
1848	2nd 8 over 6	£6	£12	£30	£60/£80
1848	2nd 8 over 7	£6	£15	£40	£75/£95
1849	380,160	£4	£9	£25	£40/£60
1849	9 struck over 8	£5	£10	£30	£60/£80
1851	594,000	£15	£50	£150	£300/----
1852	31,300	£25	£90	£200	£400/----
1853	11,880	£30	£120	£300	£600/----
1853	Grained (milled) edge proof from set		---		£300
1853	Plain edged proof (noted 1998)	"EF" . £155			----
1854	1,096,613	£2	£5	£15	£25/£36
1854	5 struck over 3	£2	£5	£18	£35/£55
1855	646,041	£2/£5	£10	£20	£40/£60
1857	Proof only, grained edge	---	---		£650
1862	Proof only, plain edge	---	---		£550
1862	Proof only, grained edge	--	---		£550
1888	JUBILEE HEAD (Br.Guiana)	£4	£8	£25	£50/£65
1888	Grained edge proof	---	---		£400/£500

GEORGE IV   SILVER 19mm

Date	Mintage/etc (ESC)	Fair/Fine	V.F.	E.F.	FDC
1820	Proof only, garnished shield	- - -			£600/£750
1821	863,280	£8	£22	£60	£125/£200
1821	Proof (1655)	- - -	- - -	- - -	- - - -/£350
1821	BBITANNIAR error	£40	£120	£500	£700/£950
1824	633,600 gartered shield	£10	£20	£60	£120/£170
1825	483,120 gartered shield	£8	£18	£45	£80/£120
1825	Pattern for BARE HEAD design (Spink)				£2,000
1826	689,040	£15	£50	£125	£250/£325
1826	A proof - Shield within Garter			- - -	£125/£250

Type change to BARE HEAD - LION-on-CROWN reverse

Date	Mintage/etc	Fair/Fine	V.F.	E.F.	FDC
1826	Included above	£5	£15	£45	£90/£125
1826	A proof - Bare Head/Lion on Crown				- - - -/£150
1827	166,320	£12	£30	£80	£165/£220
1828	15,840 ?	£4/£9	£24	£85	£130/- - - -
1829	403,920	£4/£9	£20	£80	£125/- - - -

WILLIAM IV   SILVER 19mm

Date	Mintage/etc	Fair/Fine	V.F.	E.F.	FDC
1831	1,340,195 (1670)	£6	£18	£55	£95/£150
1831	A proof - plain edge	(noted 2000)		"abt. FDC"	£160
1831	A proof with grained edge	- - -	- - -		£350
1831	A proof in palladium	- - -	- - -		£1,500
1834	5,892,480	£4	£15	£40	£80/£120
1835	1,552,320	£4	£15	£40	£90/£130
1836	1,987,920	£12	£30	£90	£120/£160
1837	506,880	£15	£35	£100	£150/£200

VICTORIA   Young Head   SILVER 19mm

Date	Mintage/etc	Fair/Fine	V.F.	E.F.	FDC
1838	1,607,760	£4	£12	£45	£75/£110
1839	3,310,560	£4	£15	£50	£75/£120
1839	A proof or pattern	(noted 2000)		"abt. FDC"	£250
1840	2,098,800	£5	£9	£38	£75/£110
1840	Pattern by W.Wyon rev cancelled with fine lines				- - -/ - - -
1841	1,386,000	£5	£18	£60	£95/£150
1841	Pattern, gold, using half-sovereign reverse				
1842	601,920	£5	£18	£60	£90/£130
1843	3,160,080	£4	£15	£50	£80/£120
1844	3,975,840	£4	£12	£40	£70/£100
1844	Has large 44	£7	£20	£75	£120/- - -

VICTORIA   Young Head

Date	Mintage/etc	Fine	V.F.	E.F.	abt. Unc/FDC
1845	3,714,480	£5	£15	£50	£90/£140
1846	4,268,880	£5	£10	£45	£70/ £90
1848	586,080	£30	£90	£300	£500/£600
1848	8 struck over 6	£30	£90	£300	£500/£600
1848	8 struck over 7	£30	£90	£300	£500/£600
1850	498,960	£5	£15	£50	£100/£150
1850	5 struck over 3 (Cooke 1998)	£35			"gdVF/VF"
1851	2,288,107	£5	£15	£40	£80/£120
1851	'Doubling' DEI|	- -	- - -	"BU"	£125
1852	904,586	£5	£15	£50	£90/£125
1853	53 higher (noted 2000)	- - -		£55	- - -/ - - -
1853	3,837,930	£5	£15	£45	£80/£120
1853	A proof	- - -	- - -	- - -	"FDC" £250
1854	840,116	£60	£250	£600	£1000/£1500
1855	1,129,084	£5	£15	£45	£90/£125
1855	A proof	- - -	- - -	- - -	£250
1856	2,779,920	£5	£15	£45	£95/£125
1856	A pattern	worded	HALF SHILLING		- - - -
1856	A pattern	worded	1/2 SHILLING		- - - -
1857	2,233,440	£5	£12	£40	£80/£120
1858	1,932,480	£5	£12	£40	£80/£120
1858	A Proof	- - -	- - -	- - -	£250
1859	4,688,640	£5	£12	£45	£90/£125
1859	9 struck over 8 (Spink 1988 GEF £145)				- - -/ - - -
1860	1,100,880	£5	£12	£42	£75/£120
1862	990,000	£25	£90	£300	£500/£600
1863	491,040	£15	£60	£200	£300/£375

NOW WITH DIE NUMBER (above date, below wreath)

Date	Mintage/etc	Fine	V.F.	E.F.	abt. Unc/FDC
1864	4,253,040	£5	£15	£50	£95/£130
1865	1,631,520	£5	£15	£50	£100/£150
1866	5,140,080	£4	£12	£45	£90/£125
1866	No die number	£20	£100	£200	- - - -/£500
1867	1,362,240	£6	£18	£60	£95/ - - -
1867	A proof	- - -	- - -	- - -	£250
1868	1,069,200	£6	£20	£65	£95/£145
1869	388,080	£6	£20	£65	£95/£145
1869	A proof	- - -	- - -	- - -	£500/- - - -
1856	Variety: longer line below PENCE - rare				
1857	Variety: longer line below PENCE - rare				

SIXPENCES

Date	Mintage	Fine	V.F.	E.F.	Unc/abt. FDC
VICTORIA (continued)					
DIE NUMBER above date, below wreath					19mm
1870	479,613	£5	£20	£80	£120/£150
1870	A proof	---	---	---	£250
1871	3,662,684	£6	£20	£45	£60/ £90
1871	A proof (noted 1996) "Plain edged Uncirc."				£800/---
1871	No die number	£6	£20	£50	£85/£125
1871	A proof without die number			---	£250/£500
1872	3,382,048 die no.	£4	£10	£30	£60/ £90
1873	4,594,733 die no.	£4	£10	£30	£60/ £90
1874	4,225,726 die no.	£4	£10	£30	£60/ £90
1875	3,256,545 die no.	£4	£10	£30	£60/ £90
1876	841,435 die no.	£6	£15	£55	£100/£150
1877	4,066,486 die no.	£4	£10	£40	£75/£100
1877	No die number	£5	£12	£40	£75/£100
1878	2,624,525 die no.	£4	£10	£40	£75/£100
1878	A proof of previous coin	---	---		£250/£400
1878	8 struck over 7 (die no.)	£20	£75	£250	----/----
1878	DRITANNIAR error	£50	£150	£250	£375/£575
1878	(noted 2001)	£45	"nearFine"	----	----/----
1879	3,326,313	£6	£15	£55	£100/£150
	DIE NUMBERS DISCONTINUED				
1879	Included above	£4	£12	£35	£65/ £95
1879	A proof	---	---	---	£200/£400
1880	Hair lock on cheek	£8	£15	£50	£100/£150
1880	No lock of hair ★	£4	£10	£25	£50/£75
1880	No lock of hair ★ ★ (Mason 2000) "BU"				---/ £60
★ ★ The reverse of this example has smaller lettering than ★					
1880	A proof	---	---	---	£150/£300
1881	6,239,447	£4	£10	£20	£40/ £65
1881	A proof	---	---	---	£175/£250
1882	759,809	£6	£18	£50	£100/£125
1883	4,986,558	£4	£10	£20	£40/ £65
1884	3,422,565	£4	£10	£20	£40/ £65
1884	Pattern bearing national emblems			---	£600
1885	4,652,771	£4	£10	£20	£40/ £65
1886	2,728,249	£4	£12	£35	£50/ £80
1886	A proof	---	---	---	£175/£200
1887	3,675,607 Young Head	£4	£9	£18	£32/ £50
1887	A proof Young Head	---	---	---	£120/£175

First Young Head 1838 to 1866 inclusive.
Second Young Head 1867 to 1880; as first but lower relief.
Third Young Head 1880 to 1887; Reverse has larger letters.

Center

A---

B---

Date	Mintage	Fair/Fine	V.F.	E.F.	abt. Unc/FDC
VICTORIA Jubilee Head					
Reverse A--- GARTERED SHIELD 'WITHDRAWN':					
1887	3,675,607	£1	£3	£5	£8/£15
1887	JEB on truncation	£10/£15	£30	£75	£125/£200
1887	R of Victoria struck over V (or I)		£75	£125/£200
1887	Proof Gartered Shield	---	---		£50/£75

Being the same size and design as the half-sovereign many were gold plated and passed as such. This led to the withdrawal of this design of sixpence.

1887	Pattern - Gartered Shield - date above crown				
Reverse --B-- CROWNED VALUE IN WREATH:					
1887	Included above	£1	£2	£6	£9/£12
1887	Proof Crowned Value in Wreath	---	£60/£90
1887	Patterns by Spink, Lion-Shield-Unicorn Reverse:				
	In gold, brass, copper, tin and aluminium.				
1888	4,197,698	£1/£3	£6	£12	£20/£30
1888	A proof	---	---	---	£115
1889	8,738,928	£1/£3	£6	£12	£20/£30
1890	9,386,955	£1/£3	£6	£14	£28/£42
1890	A proof	---	---	---	£115
1891	7,022,734	£1/£2	£5	£12	£24/£30
1892	6,245,746	£1/£2	£5	£10	£20/£30
1893	7,350,619	£50/£100	£300	£950	£1500/----
OLD or WIDOW HEAD					
1893	Included above	£1/£2	£5	£12	£20/£30
1893	A proof	---	---	£20	£40/£60
1894	3,467,704	£1/£3	£5	£16	£30/£40
1895	7,024,631	£1/£2	£5	£15	£30/£40
1896	6,651,699	£1/£2	£5	£15	£30/£40
1897	5,031,498	£1/£2	£5	£15	£30/£40
1898	5,914,100	£1/£2	£5	£16	£30/£45
1899	7,996,804	£1/£2	£5	£15	£30/£40
1900	8,984,354	£2/£4	£10	£20	£35/£50
1901	5,108,757	£1/£2	£5	£12	£20/£30

The sixpence became known as a "TANNER". The cab fare from the City of London to Tanner's Hill cost sixpence. "A Tanner One"

EDWARD VII
CROWNED SIXPENCE WITHIN WREATH · .925 SILVER 19mm

Date	Mintage	Fine	V.F.	E.F.	abt. Unc/FDC
1902	6,367,378	£3	£6	£15	£25/£30
1902	15,123 proofs with matt finish				FDC £30
1903	5,410,096	£2	£8	£20	£40/£60
1904	4,487,098	£5	£12	£35	£65/£90
1904	(noted 1999)		---	"UNC"	£80/---
1905	4,235,556	£4	£10	£25	£50/£70
1906	7,641,146	£3	£8	£20	£45/£65
1906	(noted 2000)	--	--	"abt. Unc"	£45/---
1907	8,733,673	£3	£8	£20	£45/£65
1908	6,739,491	£3	£9	£25	£50/£75
1909	6,584,017	£2	£8	£20	£40/£60
1910	12,490,724	£2	£5	£15	£20/£30
1910	(noted 1998)	--	--	"BU.FDC"	---/£35
1910	(noted 2001)	--	--	"abt.Unc"	£26/---

MODIFIED EFFIGY : in the absence of a direct comparison, the modified effigy (or modified head) can be distinguished by the initials which appear on the truncation of the neck. Before modification, the initials B.M. are placed near the centre of truncation. After modification they appear, *without stops*, well to the right thus: BM (not B.M.) The initials are those of the designer of the coin: Bertram Mackennal.

GEORGE V LION ON CROWN · SILVER 19mm .925 until 1920

Date	Mintage	Fine	V.F.	E.F.	abt. Unc/FDC
1911	9,155,310	£1	£4	£10	£20/£25
1911	6,007 proofs	--	---	---	£22/£30
1911	(noted 1998 and 2000) proof			"FDC"	---/£35
1912	10,984,129	£1	£2	£20	£35/£50
1913	7,499,833	£1	£4	£15	£32/£45
1914	22,714,602	£1	£2	£5	£9/£15
1915	15,694,597	£1	£2	£5	£9/£15
1916	22,207,178	£1	£2	£5	£9/£15
1917	7,725,475	£1	£2	£12	£24/£36
1918	27,558,743	£1	£2	£9	£12/£18
1919	13,375,447	£1	£2	£8	£18/£25
1920	14,136,287:				
1920	Silver .925	£2	£5	£15	£30/£45
1920	Silver .500	£1	£2	£8	£15/£24
1921	30,339,741	£1	£2	£6	£12/£24
1921	(noted 1999)	---	---	"Choice BU"	---/£26
1922	16,878,890	£1	£2	£7	£15/£24
1923	6,382,793	£2	£4	£15	£25/£40
1924	17,444,218	£1	£3	£8	£12/£20
1925	12,720,558	£1	£2	£6	£12/£20
1925	With new broader rim		£2	£10	£20/£30
1925	A pattern of the 1928 design in nickel				£450
1926	21,809,261	£1	£2	£9	£16/£25
1926	Modified Effigy	£1	£3	£8	£12/£18
1927	68,939,873	£1	£2	£5	£9/£15
1927	15,000 proofs Rev. new OAK/ACORN design				£12/£20
1928	23,123,384	---	£1	£5	£9/£12
1929	28,319,326	---	£1	£3	£6/£12
1930	16,990,289	---	£1	£3	£7/£10
1931	16,873,268 ★	---	£2	£4	£7/£12
1931	A proof ★	---	---	---	£175
1932	9,406,117 ★	---	£4	£8	£15/£25
1933	22,185,083 ★	---	£2	£5	£10/£15
1933	A proof ★	---	---	---	£180
1934	9,304,009 ★	---	£2	£5	£10/£15
1935	13,995,621 ★	---	£1	£4	£8/£12
1936	24,380,171 ★	---	£1	£3	£8/£12

★ these have a finer grained (milled) edge

EDWARD VIII (Duke of Windsor)

SIX LINKED RINGS of ST. EDWARD

Date	Mintage	Fine	V.F.	E.F.	Unc/ abt. FDC
1937	(noted 1989)	---	---	"abt.FDC"	£9,500
1937	(noted 1996)	---	---	"abt.FDC"	£11,000
1937	(noted 1997)	---	---	"abt.FDC"	£12,000

LION on CROWN

1937	Sterling silver proof by Maklouf			"FDC"	£20

GEORGE VI

50% SILVER, 50% ALLOY to 1946 · 19mm

Date	Mintage	Fine	V.F.	E.F.	Unc/ abt. FDC
1937	22,302,524	---	25p	£2	£3/ £5
1937	26,402 proofs	---	---		£3/ £5
1938	13,402,701	---	---	£3	£6/£12
1939	28,670,304	---	---	£2	£3/ £4
1940	20,875,196	---	---	£2	£3/ £4
1941	23,186,616	---	---	£2	£3/ £4
1942	44,942,785	---	---	£1	£2/ £3
1943	46,927,111	---	---	£1	£2/ £3
1944	37,952,600	---	---	£1	£3/ £4
1945	39,939,259	---	---	£1	£3/ £4
1946	43,466,407	---	---	£1	£2/ £3

CUPRO-NICKEL

X 1946	Proof, for new coinage, in cupro-nickel				/£400
1947	29,993,263	---	---	£1	£2/ £4
1948	88,323,540	---	---	£1	£2/ £3

Monogram GRI was changed to GRVI in 1949 when title IND: IMP: (INDAE IMPERATOR) - Emperor of India - discontinued

1949	41,355,515	---	---	£1	£3/ £5
1950	32,741,955	---	---	£2	£6/ £9
1950	17,513 proofs	---	---		£6/ £9
1951	40,399,491	---	---	£1	£2/ £5
1951	20,000 proofs	---	---		£4/ £6
1952	1,013,477	£1	£4	£10	£30/£50
1952	Proof from polished dies	---	---		£750

ELIZABETH II NATIONAL EMBLEMS INTERTWINED

Date	Mintage	Fine	V.F.	E.F.	abt. Unc/FDC
1953	70,323,876	---	---	50p	£1/ £2
1953	40,000 proofs		---	---	£3/ £5

BRITT: OMN: discontinued

1954	105,241,150	---	---	£1	£2/ £4
1955	109,929,554	---	---	20p	£1/ £2
1956	109,841,555	---	---	20p	£1/ £2
1957	105,654,290	---	---	20p	£1/ £2
1958	123,518,527	---	---	---	£1/ £2
1959	93,089,441	---	---	---	50p / £1
1960	103,288,346	---	---	---	60p / £1
1961	115,052,017	---	---	---	60p / £1
1962	178,359,637	---	---	---	50p/ £1
1963	112,964,000	---	---	---	50p/ £1
1964	152,336,000	---	---	---	50p/ £1
1965	129,644,000	---	---	---	50p/ £1
1966	175,696,000	---	---	---	50p/ £1
1966	Struck in bronze	---	---	---	£150
1966	"Mule" with Commonwealth Portrait auction 1993 £396				
1967	240,788,000	---	---	---	---/ ---
1970	750,476 proofs for LAST STERLING set £2/ £3				

Various 'pointings' have been noted:

1953	ELIZABETH - ELIZABETH
1955	SIXPENCE - SIXPENCE
1964 and 1965	REGINA - REGINA

Letters point *TO* or *BETWEEN* rim beads

Young Head

Jubilee Head

"Gothic" Head

Old, Veiled or Widow Head

"Bun" Head

Gillick Head
(Mary Gillick)

Machin Head
(Arnold Machin)

Maklouf Head
(Raphael Maklouf)

Rank-Broadley
(Ian Rank-Broadley)

EIGHTPENCES and OCTORINOS

Date		V.F.	E.F.	abt. Unc./FDC
GEORGE V	ESC refers to Seaby's "The English Silver Coinage"			
PATTERNS by HUTH	Central Star bears LEGS OF MAN			
1913 ESC 1481A	Pattern for eightpence in copper			---
ESC 1481	OCTORINO	---	---	£350/----
ESC 1481	Noted (Seaby 1990) abt.FDC			£450
1913 ESC 1482	EIGHTPENCE in silver	---		----/£450
ESC 1482A	EIGHT PENCE in copper	---		----
	(Spink 1980) in iron			£225/----

These items appear only very rarely.

Briefly: specially struck silver coins are distributed to as many old men and women as the Monarch has years; those years being 'expressed' in pence. Thus, on the Monarch's fortieth birthday, 40 men and 40 women each receive 40 pence or four Maundy sets at tenpence per set. The following year the distribution would be to 41 men and 41 women: four sets plus an extra penny. There are additonal sums, paid in conventional notes and coins, in lieu of food and clothing. The distribution takes place on Maundy Thursday: the day before Good Friday.

MAUNDY SETS

FACE VALUE TEN PENCE THE SET OF FOUR COINS

SILVER 11mm · 13mm · 16mm · 18mm

Date		V.F.	E.F.	abt. Unc./FDC
GEORGE IV				
1822		£30	£70	£120/£150
1822	A proof set (ESC 2426)			£600
1823		£25	£60	£100/£125
1824		£30	£80	£125/£140
1825		£25	£60	£100/£125
1826		£25	£60	£100/£125
1827		£25	£60	£100/£125
1828		£25	£60	£100/£125
1828	A proof set (ESC 2433)			£750
1829		£25	£60	£100/£125
1830		£25	£60	£100/£125

TENPENCES

Date		V.F.	E.F.	abt. Unc./FDC
VICTORIA One Franc				Silver 23mm
1867	Pattern - ESC 1416 ONE FRANC/TEN PENCE	£400	£800/£1200	

Date		V.F.	E.F.	abt. Unc./FDC
WILLIAM IV				
1831		£35	£90	£175/£225
1831	Proof	---	---	£250/£450
1831	Proof in gold	---		£15,000
1832		£35	£80	£120/£150
1833		£35	£80	£120/£150
1834		£35	£80	£130/£200
1835		£35	£80	£120/£150
1836		£35	£90	£175/£225
1837		£35	£90	£175/£225

Young Head VICTORIA *Young Head*

Date	Sets	EF.	abt Unc/FDC	Date	Sets	EF.	abt Unc/FDC
1838	4,158	£35	£60/£90	1872	4,328	£36	£50/£65
1838	Proofs	- - -	£200	1873	4,162	£36	£50/£65
1838	Proofs In gold		£15,000	1874	4,488	£36	£50/£65
1839	4,125	£35	£60/£90	1875	4,154	£36	£50/£65
1839	Proofs	- - -	£250	1876	4,488	£36	£50/£65
1840	4,125	£35	£60/£95	1877	4,488	£36	£50/£65
1841	2,574	£35	£65/£100	1878	4,488	£36	£50/£65
1842	4,125	£35	£60/£90	1878	Proofs	£50	£200
1843	4,158	£35	£60/£90	1879	4,488	£36	£50/£65
1844	4,158	£35	£60/£90	1879	Proofs	- - -	£1,000
1845	4,158	£35	£60/£90	1880	4,488	£36	£50/£65
1846	4,158	£35	£65/£100	1881	Proofs	- - -	£200
1847	4,158	£35	£60/£90	1882	4,488	£36	£50/£65
1848	4,158	£35	£60/£90	1883	4,488	£36	£50/£65
1849	4,158	£42	£70/£110	1884	4,488	£36	£50/£65
1850	4,158	£35	£55/£70	1885	4,488	£36	£50/£65
1851	4,158	£35	£55/£70	1886	4,488	£36	£50/£65
1852	4,158	£35	£55/£70	1887	4,488	£40	£55/£75
1853	4,158	£35	£55/£70				
1853	Proofs	- - -	£350/£500		*Jubilee Head*		
1854	4,158	£36	£50/£65	1888	4,488	£36	£50/£65
1855	4,158	£36	£50/£65	1888	Proofs	- - -	- - -
1856	4,158	£36	£50/£65	1889	4,488	£45	£55/£70
1857	4,158	£36	£55/£70	1890	4,488	£45	£55/£70
1858	4,158	£36	£55/£70	1891	4,488	£45	£55/£70
1859	4,158	£36	£55/£70	1892	4,488	£45	£55/£70
1860	4,158	£36	£50/£65				
1861	4,158	£36	£50/£65				
1862	4,158	£36	£50/£65		*Old or Widow Head*		
1863	4,158	£36	£50/£65	1893	8,976	£25	£35/£45
1864	4,158	£36	£50/£65	1894	8,976	£25	£35/£45
1865	4,158	£36	£50/£65	1895	8,877	£25	£35/£45
1867	4,158	£36	£50/£65	1896	8,476	£25	£35/£45
1867	Proofs		£265	1897	8,976	£20	£30/£40
1868	4,158	£36	£50/£65	1898	8,976	£35	£45/£60
1869	4,158	£36	£50/£65	1898★	(1994)	"FDC orig. case" £58	
1870	4,488	£36	£50/£65	1899	8,976	£35	£50/£75
1871	4,488	£36	£50/£65	1900	8,976	£50	£75/£100
1871	Proof Auct.89		£410	1901	8,976	£30	£45/£60

Original Documentation Adds Value. Add £6/£9 for contemporary dated case.
1898★ No 'official' case but there were cases "of the time" by various institutions.

EDWARD VII

Date	Sets	EF.	F.D.C. from/to
1902	8,976	£30	£35/£50
1902	"Choice orig. box"		£54
1902	15,123	matt proofs	£50
1903	8,976	£30	£40/£55
1904	8,876	£30	£40/£55
1905	8,976	£30	£40/£55

Date	Sets	EF.	F.D.C. from/to
1906	8,800	£30	£35/£40
1906	Dated octagonal case		£5
1907	8,760	£30	£35/£40
1908	8,760	£30	£35/£45
1909	1,983	£35	£45/£55
1910	1,440	£40	£50/£60

GEORGE V

Date	Sets	EF.	Unc/FDC
1911	1,768	£30	£45/£60
1911	proofs	---	£60
1912	1,246	£25	£45/£60
1913	1,228	£25	£45/£60
1914	982	£42	£55/£65
1915	1,293	£25	£45/£60
1916	1,128	£25	£45/£60
1917	1,237	£25	£45/£60
1918	1,375	£30	£45/£65
1919	1,258	£25	£40/£50
1920	1,399	£25	£45/£75
1921	1,386	£25	£40/£50
1922	1,373	£75	£100/£150
1923	1,430	£35	£45/£60

Date	Sets	EF.	Unc/FDC
1924	1,515	£25	£35/£45
1925	1,438	£25	£35/£45
1926	1,504	£25	£35/£45
1927	1,647	£25	£35/£45
1928	1,642	£25	£35/£45
1929	1,761	£25	£35/£45
1930	1,724	£25	£35/£45
1931	1,759	£25	£35/£45
1932	1,835	£25	£35/£45
1933	1,872	£25	£35/£45
1934	1,887	£25	£35/£45
1935	1,928	£30	£45/£55
1936	1,323	£35	£50/£60

Orig. Documents Add Value

GEORGE VI

Date	Sets	abt Unc/FDC	Date	Sets	abt Unc/FDC
1937	1,325	£30/£40	1945	1,355	£30/£40
1938	1,275	£30/£40	1946	1,365	£30/£40
1939	1,234	£30/£40	1947	1,375	£30/£40
1940	1,277	£30/£40	1948	1,385	£30/£40
1941	1,253	£30/£40	1949	1,395	£30/£40
1942	1,231	£30/£40	1950	1,405	£30/£40
1943	1,239	£30/£40	1951	1,468	£30/£40
1944	1,259	£30/£40	1952	1,012	£40/£50

1936	distributed by Edward VIII
1937 to 1946	.500 silver was used.
1947 to 1952	a return to Sterling silver
1949 to 1952	a change of inscription
1952	distributed by Queen Elizabeth.
1954 to 1970	a change of inscription

ELIZABETH II

Date	Complete Sets		Unc/FDC
1953	1,025	St.Paul's Cathedral	£200/£300
1953	in gold	--- (1985)	£5,750
1954	1,020	Westminster Abbey	£35/£45
1955	1,036	Southwark Cathedral	£35/£45
1956	1,088	Westminster Abbey	£35/£45
1957	1,094	St.Alban's Cathedral	£35/£45
1958	1,100	Westminster Abbey	£40/£50
1959	1,106	Windsor	£40/£50
1960	1,112	Westminster Abbey	£40/£50
1961	1,118	Rochester Cathedral	£40/£50
1962	1,125	Westminster Abbey	£40/£50
1963	1,131	Chelmsford	£40/£50
1964	1,137	Westminster	£40/£50
1965	1,143	Canterbury	£40/£50
1966	1,206	Westminster	£40/£50
1967	986	Durham	£40/£50
1968	964	Westminster	£40/£50
1969	1,002	Selby	£40/£50
1970	980	Westminster	£40/£50

NOW DECIMAL PENCE

Date	Sets		Unc/FDC
1971	1,018	Tewkesbury Abbey	£40/£50
1972	1,026	York Minster	£45/£55
1973	1,004	Westminster	£45/£55
1974	1,042	Salisbury	£45/£55

(noted 2001) offers to buy decimal sets   "FDC"   £50

MAUNDY ODDMENTS

	1d	2d	3d	4d
1822	£10	£22	£25	£30
1822	3d has small head			
1823	£10	--	--	--
1830	£10	--	--	--
1835	£10	--	--	--
1836	£9	--	--	--
1850	£6	--	--	£6
1870	£5	--	--	--
1872	£6	--	--	--
1880	£5	--	--	--
1888	£5	--	--	--
1890	--	--	--	£6
1891	--	£5	--	--
1896	--	£4	--	£6

(Virtually Mintlike)

	1d	2d	3d	4d
1898	--	--	--	£7
1900	--	£4	--	--
1902	--	£4	£12	--
1903	£9	£10	--	---
1904	£9	£5	£9	£6
1905	£9	£9	£9	---
1911	--	--	--	£9
1912	£12	£9	£12	£12
1917	£12	£12	--	---
1941	£12	---	--	---
1951	---	---	£15	---
1953	£60	£50	£50	£50

Date	Complete Sets		F.D.C.
ELIZABETH II		11mm · 13mm · 16mm · 18mm	From/ To
1975	1,050	Peterborough	£45/£55
1976	1,158	Hereford	£45/£55
1977	1,138	Westminster	£45/£55
1978	1,178	Carlisle	£40/£50
1979	1,189	Winchester	£40/£50
1980	1,198	Worcester	£40/£50
1981	1,208	Westminster	£40/£50
1982	1,218	St.David's Cathedral	£40/£50
1983	1,218	Exeter Cathedral	£40/£50
1984	1,243	Southwell Minster	£40/£50
1985	1,248	Ripon Cathedral	£40/£50
1986	1,378	Chichester Cathedral	£50/£60
1987	1,390	Ely Cathedral	£50/£60
1988	1,402	Lichfield Cathedral	£50/£60
1989	1,353	Birmingham Cathedral (63p)	£50/£60
1990	1,523	St. Nicholas Newcastle (64p)	£50/£60
1991	1,384	Westminster (65p)	£50/£60
1992	1,424	Chester (66p)	£50/£60
1993	1,440	Wells Cathedral (67p)	£50/£60
1994	1,437	Truro Cathedral (68p)	£75/£85
1995	1,466	Coventry Cathedral (69p)	£75/£85
1996		Norwich Cathedral (70p)	£75/£85
1997		Bradford Cathedral (71p)	£80/£95
1998		Portsmouth Cathedral (72p)	£80/£95
1999		Bristol Cathedral (73p)	£80/£95
2000		Lincoln Cathedral (74p)	
2001	12th April	Westminster (75p)	
2002	....		
2003	....		

Averages of Maundy Sets are influenced by V.A.T.
Thus: a set was reported as 'at auction' £65
Investigation showed £65 + Buyer's Premium of
10%, + VAT on the whole - a total of £82.23

Date	Mintage/etc (ESC)	Fair/Fine	V.F.	E.F.	abt Unc/FDC
GEORGE IV					SILVER 23mm
LAUREATE HEAD · GARNISHED SHIELD · DATE BELOW HEAD					
1820	Pattern			(1986)	£2,012
1821	2,463,120	£6/£9	£25	£75	£140/£180
1821	A proof	- - -	- - -	- - -	£400/£600
LAUREATE HEAD · GARTERED SHIELD · DATE BELOW HEAD					
1823	693,000	£15	£50	£125	£225/£350
1823	A proof	- - -	- - -	- - -	£800
1824	4,158,000	£3/£9	£20	£75	£140/£180
1824	A proof	- - -	- - -	- - -	£450
1825	2,459,160 (1253)	£8/£15	£30	£90	£145/£200
1825	A proof	- - -	- - -	- - -	£450
1825	5 struck over 3	- - -	- - -	- - -	- - - -
BARE HEAD · LION on CROWN · DATE BELOW HEAD					
1825	Included above	£2/ £6	£20	£50	£95/£125
1825	A proof	- - -	- - -	- - -	£450
1825	1 for 1 in date	- - -	- - -	- - -	£125/£200
1825	A proof struck in Barton's Metal ★			- - -	£900
1826	6,351,840 (1257)	£2/£4	£8	£30	£65/£95
1826	A proof (ESC 1258)	- - -		£95	FDC £200
1826	6 struck over a 2nd 2	- - -	£20	£60	£120
1827	574,200	£8/£15	£45	£100	£250/£300
1829	879,120	£8/£15	£30	£90	£180/£250

★ Barton's Metal is a 'sandwich' of 1 slice of copper between 2 slices of gold

WILLIAM IV

W.W. in script on truncation of neck — SILVER 23mm

Date	Mintage	Fair/Fine	V.F.	E.F.	Unc/abt FDC
1831	Proofs, plain edge, from sets			£135	£300/£400
1831	Proofs, grained (milled) edge			---	£700
1834	3,223,440	£5/£9	£20	£70	£120/£185
1834	A proof with flat topped '3' (1988)			"FDC"	£600
1834	W (block, no stops)				
1835	1,449,360	£6/£10	£30	£90	£175/£225
1836	3,567,960	£6/£10	£30	£90	£175/£225
1837	479,160	£10	£30	£100	£160/£250
1837	A proof (1984 "abt.FDC" £300)			(1997 "abt.FDC" £700)	

VICTORIA

FIRST YOUNG HEAD — SILVER 23mm

Date	Mintage	Fair/Fine	V.F.	E.F.	Unc/abt FDC
1838 W.W.	1,956,240	£6	£16	£60	£120/£150
1838 W.W.	Proofs	--	---	---	£400/£600
1839 W.W.	5,666,760	£4	£12	£40	£80/£120
1839 W.W.	Proofs, plain edged	---	---		£250

SECOND YOUNG HEAD

Date	Mintage	Fair/Fine	V.F.	E.F.	Unc/abt FDC
1839	Proof (with W.W.) from the sets				£350
1839	No W.W. at neck	£2	£12	£45	£90/£150
1839	Proof (no W.W.) grained edge			---	£750
1840	1,639,440	£3/£9	£25	£85	£125/£200
1841	875,160	£3/£9	£25	£85	£125/£200
1842	2,094,840	£9	£12	£40	£80/£120
1843	1,465,200	£10	£20	£60	£120/£180
1844	4,466,880	£9	£15	£50	£100/£150
1845	4,082,760	£9	£14	£35	£70/£100
1846	4,031,280	£9	£14	£35	£70/£100
1848 (★)	1,041,480	£30	£62	£200	£300/---
1848	(Mason 2000) "no overstrike nr. EF"				£160
1849	645,480	£9	£15	£50	£95/£150
1850	685,080	£90	£300	£925	£1,500
1850	50 over 46	£400		---	----
1850	50 over 49		---	£1500	/ ---
1851	470,071	£15 / £30	£75	£250	£450/ ---
1852	1,306,574	£8	£15	£50	£95/£140
1853	4,256,188	£7	£14	£45	£90/£120
1853	Proofs from the sets		---		£300/£500

(★) 1848 all second 8 struck over 6

VICTORIA

Date	Mintage	Fair/Fine	V.F.	E.F.	Unc/abt FDC
1854	552,414	£40	£125	£350	£700/£950
1854/1		£125	£450	£1000	---/----
1855	1,368,499	£2/£6	£15	£45	£85/£115
1856	3,168,000	£2/£6	£15	£45	£85/£115
1857	2,562,120	£2/£6	£15	£45	£85/£115
1857	REG F: 9:	(error inverted G)	£450		---/----
1858	3,108,600	£6	£15	£45	£85/£125
1858/8	(Mason 1994) "Unrecorded over-date abt. EF" £65				
1859	4,561,920	£6	£15	£45	£85/£125
1860	1,671,120	£8	£20	£60	£110/£160
1861	1,382,040	£8	£20	£60	£110/£160
1861	1 over tilted 1 (1988 near E.F. £45) ---				
1861	1 over tilted 1 (Cooke 1998) "BU deep toning" £135				
1862	954,360	£10	£40	£90	£150/£225
1863	859,320	£20	£40	£100	£200/£295
1863/1		£50	£125	£250	---/----

THE FOLLOWING HAVE A DIE NUMBER (above date)

Date	Mintage	Fair/Fine	V.F.	E.F.	Unc/abt FDC
1864	4,518,360	£2/£6	£15	£45	£85/£120
1865	5,619,240	£2/£6	£15	£45	£85/£120
----	(ESC 1398) Undated pattern (Seaby 1988) "abt.FDC" £650				
1866	4,989,600	£6	£15	£45	£80/£125
1866	(Weeks 1994) "Gem, BU/FDC proof-like" £125				
1866	BBITANNIAR error (Coin Mkt. Values 1995) "EF" £350				
1867	2,166,120	£6	£15	£45	£80/£125
1867	Proof without Die No. grained edge £500/----				
1867	Proof without Die No. plain edge £1000/----				

A specialist collection: all possible die numbers of a single date !

THIRD HEAD, larger, lower relief

Date	Mintage	Fair/Fine	V.F.	E.F.	Unc/abt FDC
1867	included above	£20	£60	£200	£350/----
1868	3,330,360	£6	£15	£45	£90/£125
1869	736,560	£9	£18	£50	£100/£150
1870	1,467,471	£9	£20	£60	£100/£150
1871	4,910,010	£5	£12	£40	£70/£100
1872	8,897,781	£5	£12	£35	£65/ £95
1873	6,489,598	£5	£12	£40	£70/£100
1874	5,503,747	£5	£12	£40	£70/£100
1874	With crosslet 4	--	£12	£40	£70/£100
1875	4,353,983	£5	£10	£30	£60/ £80
1876	1,057,487	£5	£12	£40	£90/£125
1877	2,980,703	£5	£10	£30	£50/ £75
1877	Believed to exist without Die Number				---/----
1878	3,127,131	£5	£12	£35	£65/ £95
1879	3,611,507	£20	£50	£125	£225/£325
1879	6 over 8 (Die 13) (Numis. Circ.) May, 1983				

SHILLINGS

VICTORIA
Young Head
DIE NUMBER DISCONTINUED
Reverse: CROWNED ONE SHILLING IN WREATH · SILVER 23mm

Date	Mintage	Fair/Fine	V.F.	E.F.	Unc./abt. FDC
1879	Fourth Head (Inc. page 33) £6	£12	£45	£90/---
1880	4,842,786	£2/£4	£8	£25	£50/£75
1881	5,255,332	£2/£4	£8	£25	£50/£75
1881	Shorter line below SHILLING	£8	£25	£50/£75
1882	1,611,786	£10	£30	£80	£150/---
1883	7,281,450	£2/£4	£8	£25	£45/£65
1884	3,923,993	£2/£4	£8	£25	£45/£65
1885	3,336,527	£2/£4	£8	£25	£40/£60
1886	2,086,819	£3	£6	£14	£35/£50
1887	4,034,133 Young head	£5	£18	£50	£90/£125

Jubilee Head small head to 1889
Reverse: SHIELD IN GARTER · SILVER 23mm

Date	Mintage	Fair/Fine	V.F.	E.F.	Unc./abt. FDC
1887	Included above	£1	£4	£6	£12/£18
1887	Long tailed 'Q' in 'QUE' (Cooke 2001) "abt.BU"	£22		
1887	1,084 proofs from the sets	---	£50/£75	
1888	Last 8 over 7	--	£6	£20	£40/£60
1888	4,526,856	£2	£5	£15	£25/£40
1889	7,039,628 but ★	£10/£25	£80	£275	£365/£450
1889	★ Larger head	£3	£6	£20	£40/£60
1890	8,794,042	£2	£6	£20	£40/£60
1891	5,665,348	£2/£4	£8	£25	£40/£60
1892	4,591,622	£2/£4	£6	£25	£40/£60

Proofs exist for other dates but are rarely offered.
Messrs. Seaby's "The English Silver Coinage" lists some 40 patterns.

1887 "shuttlecock" varieties : embellishment divides date - 18 ♥ 87
The device points to a rim tooth = Reverse A   Rare
The device points between two teeth = Reverse B   Common

VICTORIA
Old, Veiled or Widow Head
THREE SHIELDS within GARTER · SILVER 23mm

Date	Mintage	Fair/Fine	V.F.	E.F.	Unc/abt FDC
1893	7,039,074	£3	£6	£10	£25/£45
1893	Obv. small letters	£12	£20	£40/£60	
1893	(noted 1998)	--	---	FDC £72	
1893	1,312 proofs from the sets			£45/£65	
1894	5,953,152	£3	£6	£16	£35/£50
1895	8,880,651	£1/£4	£10	£20	£30/£45
1896	9,264,551	£1/£3	£6	£16	£25/£40
1897	6,270,364	£1/£3	£6	£20	£40/£60
1898	9,768,703	£1/£3	£6	£20	£40/£60
1899	10,965,382	£3	£6	£16	£20/£32
1900	10,937,590	£3	£6	£12	£20/£35
1901	3,426,294	£3/£5	£9	£18	£30/£45

EDWARD VII
Reverse: LION on CROWN · SILVER 23mm

Date	Mintage	Fair/Fine	V.F.	E.F.	Unc/abt FDC
1902	7,809,481	£2	£5	£20	£30/£50
1902	15,123 Proofs matt finish	---		£30/£40	
1903	2,061,823	£4	£15	£50	£95/£180
1904	2,040,161	£5	£20	£60	£120/£175
1905 (★)	488,390	£18/£40	£100	£300	£600/---
1905	(noted 2001) "abt.E.F."	£375		----/---
1906	10,791,025	£3	£6	£20	£30/£50
1907	14,083,418	£3	£6	£18	£30/£50
1908	3,806,969	£3	£12	£60	£95/£175
1909	5,664,982	£3	£12	£60	£95/£175
1910	26,547,236	£2	£8	£20	£40/£60

(★)   Such a rarity attracts the forger !!

GEORGE V

LION-on-CROWN · Date Divided · Inner Circle · SILVER 23mm

Date	Mintage	Fine	V.F.	E.F.	Unc/abtFDC
1911	20,065,901	£2	£6	£12	£22/£32
1911	6,007 proofs	---	---		£28/£35
1911	(noted 1999) proof	---		"FDC"	£40
1912	15,594,009	£2	£6	£20	£30/£50
1913	9,011,509	£2	£6	£26	£45/£70
1913	(noted 1997)	---	--	"BU"	---/£60
1913	(noted 1997)	---	--	"FDC"	---/£75
1914	23,415,843	£1	£5	£10	£20/£30
1915	39,279,024	---	£3	£6	£12/£20
1916	35,862,015	---	£3	£6	£12/£20
1917	22,202,608	---	£3	£8	£15/£25
1918	34,915,934	---	£3	£6	£12/£20
1919	10,823,824	£3	£8	£20	£40/£50

SILVER REDUCED to .500

Date	Mintage	Fine	V.F.	E.F.	Unc/abtFDC
1920	22,825,142	£2	£5	£15	£25/£32
1921	22,648,763	£2	£6	£18	£30/£50
1921	(noted 1996) "BU Gem rare, exceptional strike"				---/£60
1922	27,215,738	£2	£4	£12	£20/£30
1923	14,575,243	£1	£3	£10	£20/£30
1923	Trial Piece in nickel	---		£200	£400
1924	Trial in nickel	---	---	£200	£400
1924	9,250,095	£1	£5	£15	£20/£35
1925	A pattern in nickel	---	---		---/---
1925	(noted 1990) Lead pattern · worded MODEL £175 "nr.VF"				
1925	5,418,764	£2	£6	£25	£40/£65
1925	(noted 1999)	--	--	"Choice BU"	£70
1926	22,516,453	£1	£4	£12	£20/£36
1926	Modified Effigy	£1	£3	£9	£20/£32
1927	9,262,344	£1	£5	£15	£25/£35

Obverse 1 = above B.M. the neck is hollow.

Reverse A = GEORGIVS (I points *BETWEEN* beads)

Obverse 2 = above B.M. the neck is flat.

Reverse B = GEORGIVS (I points *TO* a bead)

1911 Varieties: 1 + A; 1 + B; 2 + A; 2 + B.
1912 Varieties: IMP closely spaced; I M P widely spaced.
1920 Varieties: Obverse 1; Obverse 2.

GEORGE V   50% SILVER - 50% ALLOY

LION-on-CROWN · DATE at RIGHT · No inner circle

Date	Mintage	Fine	V.F.	E.F.	Unc/abtFDC
1927	NEW DESIGN	£1	£2	£9	£18/£25
1927	15,000 proofs	---	---	---	£20/£30
1928	18,136,778	---	£1	£5	£10/£15
1929	19,343,006	---	£1	£5	£10/£15
1930	3,137,092	£2	£6	£20	£40/£60
1931	6,993,926	£1	£2	£6	£12/£20
1932	12,168,101	£1	£2	£5	£10/£15
1933	11,511,624	---	£2	£6	£12/£20
1934	6,138,463	£1	£2	£10	£20/£30
1935	9,183,462	---	£1	£5	£10/£15
1936	11,910,613	---	£1	£5	£10/£15

EDWARD VIII   (Duke of Windsor)

Reverse: LION SEJANT GUARDANT

Date			
1936	few "Scottish" no "English" "Guesstimate"	£18,000
1937	COAT of ARMS silver proof by Maklouf "FDC"	£22

GEORGE VI   50% SILVER/50% ALLOY until 1947

(V.F. column marked "Bullion Value only" across these rows)

Date	Mintage	Fine	V.F.	E.F.	Unc/abtFDC
1937E	8,359,122	---		£2	£5/£6
1937E	26,402 proofs	---		---	£8
1937S	6,748,875	---		£2	£4/£5
1937S	26,402 proofs	---		---	£5/£8
1938E	4,833,436	---		£3	£9/£15
1938E	4,797,852	---		£3	£9/£15
1939E	11,052,677	---		£1	£4/£6
1939S	10,263,892	---		£1	£4/£6
1940E	11,099,126	---		£1	£4/£6
1940S	9,913,089	---		£1	£4/£6
1941E	11,391,883	---		£1	£4/£6
1941S	8,086,030	---		£2	£5/£7
1942E	17,453,643	---		£1	£3/£4
1942S	13,676,759	---		£1	£3/£6
1943E	11,404,213	---		£1	£3/£5
1943S	9,824,214	---		£1	£3/£5
1944E	11,586,752	---		£1	£3/£4
1944S	10,990,167	---		£1	£3/£5
1945E	15,143,404	---		60p	£2/£4
1945S	15,106,270	---		75p	£2/£4
1946E	18,663,797	---		75p	£2/£3
1946E	Pattern, proof, or trial in cupro-nickel				£750
1946S	16,381,501	---	---	£1	£3/£4
1947E	12,120,611	---	---	£1	£4/£6
1947S	12,282,223	---	---	£1	£4/£6
1948E	45,576,923	---	---	£1	£3/£5
1948S	45,351,937	---	---	£1	£3/£5

SHILLINGS

GEORGE VI (continued)

Date	Mintage		Fine	V.F.	E.F.	Unc. from/to
					CUPRO-NICKEL 23mm	
1949E	19,328,405		---	---	£1	£5/£7
1949S	21,243,074		---	---	£2	£6/£9
1950E	19,243,872		---	---	£5	£10/£15
1950E	17,513	proofs	---	---	---	F.D.C £10
1950S	14,299,601		---	---	£5	£10/£15
1950S	17,513	proofs	---	---	---	F.D.C £10
1951E	9,956,930		---	---	£1	£5/£7
1951E	20,000	proofs	---	---	---	F.D.C £7
1951S	10,961,174		---	---	£2	£5/£7
1951S	20,000	proofs	---	---	---	F.D.C £8
1952E	(★)	1 known outside Royal Collection				
1952E	(★)	This may be a proof of that date (Coincraft '97)				£8,000 ✗

Suffix E = English; and S = Scottish. In 1937 these coins were struck with English, and Scottish, symbols and were circulated, generally, throughout the United Kingdom. The practice continued until 1966; and for 1970.

Some Heraldic terms:
RAMPANT - such as lion rampant, see reverse of upper 1953.
STATANT GUARDANT - see left-hand 1937 and right-hand 1951.
PASSANT GUARDANT - the three leopards, lower 1953.
SEJANT GUARDANT - sideways, facing: 1937 and adjoining 1951.

Passant guardant is sometimes described as couchant (lying down), but the raised paw indicates otherwise. The three leopards are still referred to as such on old coinage, but on modern strikings are likely to be referred to as three lions.

1946E	Reverse A IND	Reverse B IND

A 'I' points TO a rim bead, B BETWEEN two beads.

ELIZABETH II

Date	Mintage		Fine	V.F.	E.F.	Unc. from/
					CUPRO-NICKEL 23mm	
1953E	41,942,894		---	---	30p	60p/£
1953	Head both sides, undated but BRITT.OMN					£30
1953E	40,000	proofs	---	---	FDC	£6
1953S	20,663,528		---	---	30p	£1/£
1953S	40,000	proofs	---	---	FDC	£6
	BRITT. OMN discontinued					
1954E	30,262,032		---	---	45p	£2/£
1954S	26,771,735		---	---	36p	£2/£
1955E	45,259,908		---	---	36p	£2/£
1955S	27,950,906		---	---	50p	£3/£
1956E	44,907,008		---	---	£2	£6/£1
1956S	42,853,637		---	---	£2	£6/£1
1957E	42,774,217		---	---	25p	£2/£
1957E	V.I.P. proof		---	---	FDC	£20
1957S	17,959,988		---	---	£3	£12/£1
1957S	V.I.P. proof		---	---	FDC	£200
1958E	14,392,305		---	---	£3	£10/£1
1958S	40,822,557		---	---	25p	£1/£
1959E	19,442,778		---	---	25p	£1/£
1959S	1,012,988		15p	50p	£3	£12/£1
1960E	27,027,914		---	---	25p	£1/£
1960S	14,376,932		---	---	25p	£1/£2
1961E	39,816,907		---	---	15p	£1/£
1961E	A proof	(offered 1998)			"FDC"	£165
1961S	2,762,558		---	10p	75p	£3/£6
1961S	A proof	(offered 1984)			"FDC"	£200
1962E	36,704,379		---	---	---	50p/£1
1962S	18,967,310		---	---	---	50p/£1
1963E	44,714,000		---	---	---	50p/£1
1963S	32,300,000		---	---	---	20p/40p
1964E	8,590,900		---	---	---	30p/50p
1964S	5,239,100		---	---	---	50p/75p
1965E	9,216,000		---	---	---	30p/75p
1965S	2,774,000		---	---	---	50p/£1
1966E	15,005,000	includes 3,000 minted in 1967				45p/£1
1966S	15,607,000	includes 3,000 minted in 1967				45p/£1
1966S	Head/Tail reversed ↑↓		---	---		£30/£50
1968	Decimal equivalent FIVE NEW PENCE introduced					
1970E	750,476	proofs LAST STERLING set				£1.50/£3
1970S	750,476	proofs LAST STERLING set				£1.50/£3

GODLESS (having no DEI GRATIA)   SILVER 28mm

	Fine	V.F.	E.F.	Unc/abtFDC
1848 (ESC799) Plain edge proof	---	---		£1600 X
1848 As above but with grained (milled) edge				£500/£600
1848 (ESC886) Plain edge pattern (2001nr. FDC)				£495
1849 413,830 'Godless'	£12	£25	£75	£125/£165

GOTHIC · date appears in Roman · third column · 30mm.

1851	1,540	mdcccli	£2000 (report 1995)	----/----
1852	1,014,552	mdcclii	£12	£30	£90	£150/£200
1852	ii struck over i	(Messrs. Weeks 1993)	£95	"abtEF"
1853	* 3,919,950	mdccliii	£10	£40	£95	£175/£300
1853	Proof		----	----	----	£800/£1000 ✗
1854	550,413	mdccliv	£200 £500 £1800	----/----
1855	831,017	mdccclv	£10	£25	£100	£175/£250
1856	* 2,201,760	mdccclvi	£10	£26	£110	£200/£275
1857	1,671,120	mdccclvii	£10	£25	£100	£150/£250
1857	Proof (ESC815)		----	----	----	£875
1858	+ 2,239,380	mdccclviii	£10	£25	£100	£150/£200
1858	(Seaby 1989) "no stop after date"	£110	"EF/gdEF"
1859	+ 2,568,060	mdccclix	£10	£25	£100	£150/£200
1860	1,475,100	mdccclx	£10	£30	£125	£200/£300
1862	594,000	mdccclxii	£20	£100	£300	£400/£600
1863	938,520	mdccclxiii	£40	£150	£500	£950/£1400 ✗
1864	1,861,200	mdccclxiv	£10	£25	£100	£175/£250
1865	! 1,580,044	mdccclxv	£10	£30	£105	£175/£225
1865	! (Mason 1994)		"abt.UNC"	£110/----
1866	! 914,760	mdccclxvi	£10	£25	£125	£180/£250
1867	. 423,720	mdccclxvii	£15	£60	£200	£340/£450
1868	896,940	mdccclxviii	£10	£30	£125	£180/£250
1869	297,000	mdccclxix	£10	£25	£100	£150/£250
1870	1,080,648	mdccclxx	£10	£25	£100	£150/£250
1871	3,425,605	mdccclxxi	£10	£25	£100	£150/£200
1872	7,199,690	mdccclxxii	£10	£25	£80	£120/£175
1873	5,921,839	mdccclxxiii	£10	£25	£80	£140/£200
1874	1,642,630	mdccclxxiv	£10	£25	£80	£140/£200
1874	iv struck over iii		£25	£60	(noted 1999)
1875	1,117,030	mdccclxxv	£10	£30	£100	£150/£200
1876	580,034	mdccclxxvi	£10	£30	£100	£165/----
1877	682,292	mdccclxxvii	£10	£30	£100	£165/----
1877	No WW (48 arcs)		£15	£60	£200	----/----
1877	No WW (42 arcs)		£12	£50	£120	£190/----
1878	1,786,680	mdccclxxviii	£10	£25	£100	£150/£200

	Fine	V.F.	E.F.	abt. Unc/FDC
1879 1,512,247	mdccclxxix				
Die No. 48 arcs WW (ESC849B)	£30	£80	----	----/----
No Die No. 42 arcs (ESC 850)	£20	£70	(no WW)	----/----
No Die No. 48 arcs WW (ESC 851)	£10	£30	£120	£165/£250
No WW 38 arcs (ESC 852)	£10	£25	£100	£150/£200
1880 Younger portrait		extremely rare		----/----
1880 2,167,170 mdccclxxx	£9	£24	£90	£150/£225
1880 (noted 1997)	--	"VF+"	£60	----/----
1881 2,570,337 mdccclxxxi	£4	£22	£75	£150/£225
1881 Broken die mdccclxxxi	£10	£45	£95	£150/£225
1883 3,555,667 mdccclxxxiii	£4	£22	£90	£150/£225
1884 1,447,379 mdccclxxxiv	£4	£22	£90	£150/£225
1885 1,758,210 mdccclxxxv	£7	£22	£90	£150/£225
1886 591,773 mdccclxxxvi	£4	£22	£90	£150/£225
1887 1,776,903 mdccclxxxvii	£7	£30	£130	£225/£300

Those above and at left are inscribed: one tenth of a pound
Proofs exist for many dates; they are rare and rarely offered

> ★ Have varieties with no stop after date.   Rarity R2
> + Have varieties with no stop after date.   Rarity R
> ! With colon after date: 1865 R3; 1866 R2
> 1867 brit: is normal; proofs/patterns have britt:
> R = rare;   R2 = very rare;   Seaby/Rayner scale.

Date

Jubilee Head (see page 28)   29.5mm

1887	Included above £2	£5	£9	£15/£25
1887	1,084 Jubilee Head proofs	£40		£80/£125
1888	1,541,540	£2	£4	£15	£30/£50
1889	2,973,561	£2/£3	£5	£18	£35/£60
1890	1,684,737	£4	£15	£60	£85/£150
1891	836,438	£10	£40	£100	£150/£225
1892	283,401	£12	£40	£95	£140/£200

Old, Veiled or Widow Head (see page 28)   28.5mm

1893	1,666,103	£2	£6	£25	£50/£75
1893	1,312 proofs	---	---	---/£125
1894	1,952,842	£3	£8	£30	£50/£75
1895	2,182,968	£3	£8	£28	£45/£70
1896	2,944,416	£3	£8	£28	£45/£70
1897	1,699,921	£2/£3	£6	£30	£45/£70
1898	3,061,343	£3	£6	£25	£45/£70
1899	3,966,953	£2	£5	£25	£40/£60
1900	5,528,630	£2	£5	£25	£40/£60
1901	2,648,870	£2	£6	£30	£45/£70

EDWARD VII

Date	Mintage	Fine	V.F.	E.F.	abt. Unc/FDC
STANDING BRITANNIA · SILVER 28.5mm					
1902	2,189,575	£5	£9	£25	£45/£65
1902	(noted 1999)		--	"BU, Gem"	£60
1902	15,123 matt finished proofs				£40/£50
1903	1,995,298	£5	£25	£55	£80/£120
1904	2,769,932	£10	£30	£90	£150/£200
1905	1,187,596	£20	£80	£250	£400/£500
1905	(noted 2000)		"gd. E.F."	£240	--
1906	6,910,128	£5	£10	£50	£100/£150
1907	5,947,895	£5	£12	£70	£90/£140
1908	3,280,010	£6	£18	£90	£140/£200
1909	3,482,289	£6	£18	£90	£140/£200
1909	(noted 2001)		---	"Mint State"	£300
1910	5,650,713	£5	£10	£50	£75/£95

GEORGE V

Date	Mintage	Fine	V.F.	E.F.	Unc/FDC
SHIELDS/SCEPTRES in Quarters · 28.5mm					
1911	5,951,284	£2	£5	£25	£40/£60
1911	6,007 proofs		---	£30	£40/£60
1912	8,571,731	£4	£8	£40	£60/£85
1913	4,545,278	£5	£15	£45	£80/£100
1914	21,252,701	£2	£6	£12	£20/£30
1915	12,367,939	£2	£3	£12	£24/£36
1916	21,064,337	£2	£6	£12	£24/£36
1917	11,181,617	£2	£6	£20	£30/£50
1918	29,211,792	£2	£6	£10	£20/£30
1919	9,469,292	£2	£6	£15	£30/£45

FROM 1920 SILVER REDUCED TO 50%					
1920	15,387,833	£2	£7	£20	£40/ £50
1921	34,863,895	£3	£7	£15	£30/ £45
1922	23,861,044	£3	£7	£15	£30/ £45
1923	21,546,533	£3	£7	£15	£28/ £40
1924	4,582,372	£3	£9	£25	£50/ £75
1925	1,404,136	£10	£30	£90	£135/£210

1911	Two obverses (see page 9)
1914	Large rim teeth and small rim teeth
1920	BRITT and BRITT (rim pointings)

FLORINS (Two Shillings)

GEORGE V

Date	Mintage	Fine	V.F.	E.F.	Unc/FDC
0·500 silver 28.5mm					
1925	Uniface lead pattern lead (Seaby 1990)			"vf+"	£225
1926	5,125,410	£3	£9	£25	£60/£75
1927	15,000 proofs of new design				£40/£65
1928	11,087,186	£2	£4	£8	£12/£18
1929	16,397,279	£2	£4	£7	£10/£15
1929	(noted 2001)		---	"FDC"	£25
1930	5,753,568	£2	£4	£8	£12/£18
1931	6,556,331	£2	£4	£7	£10/£18
1932	717,041	£10	£20	£80	£125/£225
1933	8,685,303	£2	£4	£8	£16/£30
1934	none	---	---	---	---/---
1935	7,540,546	£1	£3	£6	£9/£15
1936	9,897,448	£1	£2	£4	£8/£12

EDWARD VIII as GEORGE VI but monogram ER

1937	"Guesstimate"	£12,000/£15,000
1937	Pattern in sterling silver by Maklouf FDC £25	

GEORGE VI

Date	Mintage	Fine	V.F.	E.F.	Unc/FDC
50/50 silver/alloy until 1947					
1937	13,006,781	50p	£2	£3	£4/£6
1937	26,402 proofs		---		£8/£10
1938	7,909,388	50p	£3	£8	£16/£20
1939	20,850,607	50p	£2	£4	£6/£8
1939	Proof	---	---	(Spinks 1986)	/£165
1940	18,700,338	50p	£2	£3	£4/£5
1941	24,451,079	50p	£2	£3	£4/£5
1942	39,895,243	50p	£2	£3	£4/£5
1943	26,711,987	50p	£2	£3	£4/£5
1944	27,560,005	50p	£1	£3	£3/£4
1945	25,858,049	50p	£1	£2	£3/£4
1946	22,910,085	50p	£1	£2	£4/£5

CUPRO-NICKEL

Date	Mintage	Fine	V.F.	E.F.	Unc/FDC
1946	Trial Piece, new coinage, cupro-nickel,				--/---
1947	22,910,085	---	---	£2	£4/£5
1948	67,553,636	---	---	£1	£2/£4
1949	28,614,939	---	---	£2	£4/£8
1949	Proof	---	---	---	£160/---
1950	24,357,490	---	---	£2	£8/£15
1950	17,513 proofs		FDC		£15
1951	27,411,747	---	---	£3	£6/£9
1951	20,000 proofs	---	FDC		£10

Cupro-Nickel 28.5 mm FLORINS (Two Shillings)

ELIZABETH II

		Fine	V.F.	E.F.	abt. Unc / FDC
1953	11,958,710	---	---	£1	£2/£4
1953	40,000 proofs	---	---	---	£4/£6

BRITT: OMN: not now included in legend

(Glendinings 2000) Rev. TRIAL DIE £460

1954	13,085,422	---	---	£5	£25/£35
1955	25,887,253	---	---	£2	£3/£5
1956	47,824,500	---	---	£2	£3/£5
1957	33,071,282	---	---	£4	£20/£30
1957	(noted '98 and '99)	"V.I.P. proof FDC"			£250
1958	9,564,580	---	---	£2	£6/£12
1958	(noted '97 and '99)	"V.I.P. proof FDC"			£250
1959	14,080,319	---	---	£5	£10/£15
1960	13,831,782	---	---	£1	£2/£3
1961	37,735,315	---	---	£1	£2/£3
1961	(noted 1999)	"V.I.P. proof FDC"			£230
1962	35,147,903	---	---	50p	£1/£3
1963	25,562,000	---	---	50p	£1/£3
1964	16,539,000	---	---	50p	£1/£3
1965	48,163,000	---	---	50p	£1/£2
1966	84,041,000	---	---	50p	£1/£2
1967	22,152,000	---	---	50p	£1/£2
1967	Two tails: reverse both sides			£75	£95/£125
1968	17,566,000 dated 1967. Decimals introduced.				
1970	750,476 proofs Last Sterling set		---		£2/£3

Continued on page 49 under DECIMAL COINAGE

Silver 32 mm HALF CROWNS

GEORGE IV

		Fine	V.F.	E.F.	Unc/abtFDC
1820	Garnished Shield	£9	£30	£95	£180/£275
1821	1,435,104 Rev.1	£12	£32	£95	£180/£290
1821	(*) Rev.2	£15	£60	£300	£400/----
1821	Proof	---	---	£300	£600/£950
1822	Proof (only 2 known)	(1993)		"FDC"	£3,650
1823	2,003,760	£225	£650	£1800	£3,000
1823	Shield in Garter	£9	£35	£120	£250/£375
1823	Pattern (ESC 652)	(1991)		"FDC"	£4,800
1824	465,696 ?	£14	£60	£180	£260/£350
1824	Bare Head	£500	£750	£2650	----/----
1825	2,258,784	£10	£30	£90	£160/£200
1825	Proofs (ESC 643; and 644)				/£850
1825	Proof (ESC 645) in Barton's Metal : a 'sandwich' of one slice of copper and two thin slices of gold. (1984) £1,500				
1826	2,189,088	£9	£35	£120	£200/£325
1826	Proofs from the sets		---	£150	----/£700
1828	49,890 ?	£12	£50	£120	£200/£325
1829	508,464	£12	£50	£180	£260/£350
	Proofs except 1828 and 1829; patterns 1820/22/23/24				
	Pattern "Binfield" (ESC 655) (1991) " abt.Unc."				£395/----

(*) 1821 Rev.2 subtle differences, e.g. examine shamrock stems

WILLIAM IV

Silver 32 mm

		Fine	V.F.	E.F.	Unc/abtFDC
1831	Currency	£600 (Coincraft Cat. 1997)			----/----
1831	Proofs from the sets	(noted 2001)			£600
1834	993,168 WW	£15	£60	£240	£400/£650
1834	Proof WW	---	---	---	£950/£1200
1834	W W in script	£7	£30	£110	£200/£290
1834	Proof W W	---	---	---	£950/£1200
1834	Proof W W plain edged	---	---	---	£2000/£3000
1835	281,952	£12	£50	£150	£300/£450
1836	1,588,752	£6	£25	£110	£200/£300
1836	6 struck over 5	£12	£50	£150	£250/£325
1837	150,526	£12	£50	£150	£250/£360

HALF CROWNS

VICTORIA Young Head — SILVER 32 mm

	Mintage	Fine	V.F.	E.F.	Unc/abtFDC
1839a	Raised WW	- - - -	£400	£800	£3000
1839a	Proof with grained (milled) edge				- - - - /£2500
1839a	Proof with plain edge, from the sets				- - - - / £600
1839a	(noted 1998) "virtually FDC · pink/blue tones"				£695
1839b	Proof with two ornamented hair fillets				- - - - /£1500
1839c	Proof with two plain hair fillets				- - - - /£3500
1839d	Currency,	£350	£750	£2000	£3000/- - - -
1839d	Proof, grained (milled) edge			- - -	- - - - /£3000
1839d	Plain edge proofs, from the sets			- - -	- - - - /£4500
1840	386,496	£25	£80	£200	£300/£450
1841	42,768	£250	£500	£1500	£2200/- - - -
1842	486,288	£20	£50	£160	£250/£375
1843	454,608	£55	£140	£550	£650/£900
1844	1,999,008	£12	£40	£125	£230/£300
1845	2,231,856	£10	£35	£100	£175/£275
1846	1,539,668	£15	£45	£120	£200/£300
1846	8 struck over 1	£16	£50	£160	£300/£375
1846	8 struck over 7	£60	£200	£600	£1200/- - - -
1848	367,488 2nd 8/6	£30	£120	£360	£475/£650
1849	261,360 large date	£15	£50	£200	£300/£400
1849	Smaller date	£30	£100	£300	£750/£950
1850	484,613	£15	£55	£200	£350/£450
1853	Proofs from the sets (ESC 687)			- - -	£1,500
1862	Proofs (ESC 688) and (ESC 689)			- - -	£2,500
1864	Proof only, for the Albert Memorial			- - -	£3,000
1874	2,188,599	£10	£25	£80	£160/£225
1875	1,113,483	£10	£25	£75	£145/- - - -
1876	633,221	£12	£30	£80	£150/- - - -
1876	6 struck over 5	£18	£40	£125	£200/- - - -
1877	447,059	£12	£30	£65	£100/£150
1878	1,466,232	£10	£25	£75	£100/£150
1879	901,356	£16	£30	£100	£140/£220
1879	Proof (Seaby 1990) (ESC704)			"abt.FDC"	£1100
1880	1,346,350	£12	£28	£70	£110/£160
1881	2,301,495	£10	£25	£60	£100/£150
1882	808,227	£12	£25	£75	£125/£200
1883	2,982,779	£12	£28	£80	£120/£200
1884	1,569,175	£10	£25	£75	£120/£200
1885	1,628,438	£12	£28	£75	£120/£200
1886	891,767	£12	£28	£75	£120/£200
1887	261,747 Yng. Head	£10	£30	£90	£180/£250

(a) has one plain, one ornamented hair fillet; WW, on neck, is raised
(b) has two ornamental hair fillets: WW raised
(c) has two plain hair fillets; WW raised
(d) has two plain hair fillets; WW incuse (struck in)

VICTORIA Jubilee Head — SILVER 32mm

Date	Mintage	Fine	V.F.	E.F.	Unc/abtFDC
1887	1,176,299	£3	£7	£14	£20/£30
1887	1,084 proofs	- - -			£125/£145
1888	1,428,787	£4	£9	£30	£50/£75
1889	4,811,954	£4	£9	£30	£45/£70
1890	3,228,111	£4	£12	£40	£60/£95
1891	2,284,632	£4	£12	£40	£60/£95
1892	1,710,946	£4	£12	£40	£60/£95

Old, Veiled or Widow Head

Date	Mintage	Fine	V.F.	E.F.	Unc/abtFDC
1893	1,792,600	£4	£8	£25	£50/£70
1893	1,312 proofs	- - -	- - -		£120
1894	1,524,960	£5	£12	£60	£80/£95
1895	1,772,662	£5	£12	£50	£75/£90
1896	2,148,505	£5	£12	£50	£75/£90
1897	1,678,643	£4	£10	£30	£50/£70
1898	1,870,055	£4	£10	£40	£60/£80
1899	2,863,872	£4	£10	£40	£60/£80
1900	4,479,128	£4	£10	£40	£55/£75
1901	1,516,570	£4	£10	£40	£55/£75

Several patterns, proofs and varieties occur.

EDWARD VII — SILVER 32mm

Date	Mintage	Fine	V.F.	E.F.	Unc/abtFDC
1902	1,316,008	£8	£16	£40	£60/£80
1902	15,123 matt surfaced proofs				£50/£70
1903	274,840	£40	£120	£375	£500/£800
1904	709,652	£35	£110	£275	£400/£600
1905	166,008	£120	£300	£750	£950/£1300
1905	(S & B '95)	£150 "Fine/nearly VF"			- - - -/- - -
1906	2,886,206	£8	£25	£60	£100/£175
1906	(S & B '95)	"nr.UNC, nice tone" £95			
1907	3,693,930	£8	£25	£80	£120/£180
1908	1,758,889	£10	£30	£120	£160/£225
1909	3,051,592	£8	£25	£75	£140/£225
1910	2,557,685	£8	£25	£65	£95/£150

Date	Mintage	Fine	V.F.	E.F.	Unc/ abtFDC.
GEORGE V				SILVER to 1920 32mm	
1911	2,914,573	£3	£9	£25	£50/£75
1911	6,007 proofs		- - -		£60/£70
1911	(noted 1998)	- -	- - -	"FDC"	£75
1912	4,700,789	£4	£10	£30	£55/£85
1913	4,090,160	£4	£10	£45	£90/£180
1914	18,333,003	£4	£10	£15	£20/£30
1915	32,433,066	£2	£4	£10	£16/£25
1916	29,530,020	£3	£6	£12	£24/£30
1917	11,172,052	£3	£6	£12	£25/£35
1918	29,079,592	£3	£6	£12	£24/£36
1919	10,266,737	£3	£6	£15	£45/£70
NOW REDUCED TO .500 SILVER					
1920	17,983,077	£2	£5	£20	£45/£70
1921	23,677,889 DEI	£2	£5	£25	£45/£70
1921	DEI	£2	£5	£25	
1922	16,396,774 Rev. A	£6	£20	£25	£35/£50
	Rev. B	£8	£25		£40/£60
Rev.A = Narrow groove between crown and shield					
Rev.B = Wide groove between crown and shield					
1923	26,308,526	£2	£5	£10	£20/£30
1924	5,866,294	£2	£6	£25	£50/£75
1925	1,413,461	£4	£15	£100	£165/£265
1926	4,473,516	£2	£5	£30	£60/£90
1926	No colon after OMN	£25	£165		£260/- - - -
1926	Modified Effigy	£2	£6	£30	£55/£80
1927	6,852,872	£2	£5	£15	£30/£45
1927	15,000 proofs, new design		- - -		£20/£30
1928	18,762,727	£2	£5	£8	£16/£25
1929	17,632,636	£2	£5	£8	£16/£25
1930	809,501	£6	£15	£75	£150/£225
1931	11,264,468	£2	£5	£10	£18/£25
1932	4,793,643	£2	£5	£15	£30/£50
1933	10,311,494	£2	£5	£10	£18/£25
1934	2,422,399	£2	£5	£25	£40/£70
1935	7,022,216	£2	£5	£10	£15/£20
1935	A proof changed hands in 1975 for				£160/- - - -
1936	7,039,423	£2	£5	£9	£12/£18

1928 Rosette: ⋆ = Rev. A; ⋆⋆ = Rev. B
1929 Varieties as for 1928

EDWARD VIII *(Duke of Windsor)* ·500 SILVER
1937 Standard bearing ROYAL ARMS (1993) £16,000/£20,000 ✗
1937 Sterling Silver ROYAL ARMS by Maklouf FDC £25

Date	Mintage	Fine	V.F.	E.F.	abt. Unc/ FDC
GEORGE VI .500 SILVER until 1947					
1937	9,106,440	£1	£2	£3	£6/£9
1937	26,402 proofs		- -	FDC	£10
1938	6,426,478	£1	£2	£6	£18/£24
1938	(noted 1996)	"FDC superb"	- -		£25
1939	15,478,635	£1	£2	£3	£6/£9
1940	17,948,439	£1	£2	£3	£6/£9
1941	15,773,984	£1	£2	£3	£6/£9
1942	31,220,090	£1	£2	£3	£6/£9
1943	15,462,875	£1	£2	£3	£6/£9
1944	15,255,165	£1	£2	£3	£6/£9
1945	19,849,242	£1	£2	£3	£5/£8
1946	22,724,873	£1	£2	£3	£5/£8
NOW CUPRO-NICKEL (no silver)					
1946	Proof (in cupro-nickel)	- -	- -		£1,250 ✗
1947	21,911,484	- -	£1	£2	£4/£6
1948	71,164,703	- -	£1	£2	£4/£6
1949 ⋆	28,272,512	- -	£2	£3	£5/£8
1950	28,335,500	- -	£1	£2	£8/£12
1950	17,513 proofs	- -	- -	FDC	£12
1951	9,003,520	- -	£1	£3	£6/£9
1951	20,000 proofs	- -	- -	FDC	£8
1952	1 Sold by "Private Treaty" in 1991 £28,500				

⋆ IND: IMP (Emperor of India) discontinued from 1949

HALF CROWNS

Date	Mintage	Fine	V.F.	E.F.	abt. Unc/FDC.
ELIZABETH II			CUPRO-NICKEL 32mm		
1953	4,333,214	--	DEI ..	£1	£2/£3
1953	I points between rim beads		DEI	£1	£3/£6
1953	40,000 proofs	--	--	FDC	---/£7
1954	11,614,953	--	--	£4	£15/£25
1954	Proof	(1985 £225)		(1999 £325)	
1955	23,628,726	--	--	£1	£4/£6
1956	33,934,909	--	--	£2	£6/£8
1957	34,200,563	--	--	£1	£2/£4
1958	15,745,668	--	--	£3	£12/£20
1959	9,028,844	--	--	£4	£15/£25
1960	19,929,191	--	--	£1	£3/£4
1961	25,887,897	--	--	--	£2/£3
1961	Struck on polished dies (or blanks)				£4/£6
1962	24,013,312	--	--	--	£1/£2
1963	17,557,600	--	--	--	£1/£2
1964	5,973,600	--	--	£1	£2/£4
1965	9,878,400	--	--	--	£1/£3
1966	13,384,000	--	--	--	70p/£2
1967	18,895,200	--	--	--	60p/£1
1968	14,163,200 but dated 1967 · Total 33,058,400				
1969	Halfcrowns were demonetized 31st December.				
1970	Proofs from the 8-coin set	--			£2/£4

Four Shillings) DOUBLE FLORINS

Date	Mintage	Fine	V.F.	E.F.	abt. Unc/FDC.
VICTORIA		Jubilee Head		SILVER 36mm	
1887	483,347 Roman I	£5	£15	£25	£35/£50
1887	Roman I proof	--	--	---	£95/£150
1887	Arabic 1 in date	£5	£15	£25	£40/£60
1887	Arabic 1 proof	--	--	---	£95/£150
1888	243,340	£6	£15	£30	£60/£90
1888 ★	Inverted 1 for second I	£15	£40	£80	£120/£180
1889	1,185,111	£5	£10	£20	£40/£60
1889 ★	Inverted 1 for second I	£15	£40	£80	£120/£180
1890	782,146	£6	£12	£25	£60/£90
1890	Pattern with reverse worded DOUBLE FLORIN				

★ 2nd I of VICTORIA appears as I

J.E.B. at truncation = Designer/Engraver Joseph Boehm

GEORGE V
SILVER 36mm
1910	Double Florin in gold (1986)	£5,700
1911	Rare Plain and grained edge patterns (sundry metals)	
1911	As picture but DOUBLE FLORIN (1989 abtFDC £450)	
1914	worded: TWELVE GROATS and in various metals	

GEORGE VI
SILVER 36mm
1950 Patterns, grained edge, George and Dragon ext. rare
1950 As previous but 'FOUR SHILLINGS' struck into the edge

GEORGE IV

LAUREATE HEAD · St. George/Dragon Reverse · Silver 38.61mm

1820	Pattern (ESC 259)	(Dolphin 1993) "FDC"	£5000	✗
1821	437,976 SECVNDO £20	£70	£300	£650/£800
1821	SECVNDO proof	(noted 1999) £2600	----/----
1821	Error TERTIO proof (noted 1999)	----	£3800	✗
1822	124,929 SECVNDO £20	£80	£350	£850/£1200
1822	SECVNDO proof ---	(noted 1999)	£3600	
1822	TERTIO £20	£70	£320	£650/£900
1822	TERTIO proof ---	(noted 1986)	£2300
1823	Without edge number, proof only (offers to buy £6000)

Bare Head · Shield Reverse

1825	(ESC 255) BARE HEAD pattern	(noted 1996)	£5000 ✗
1826	(ESC 257) SEPTIMO proof from the sets (1987)	£3000 ✗
1828	(ESC 263) Pattern in Germanic style	£500 (1998) -----

WILLIAM IV

MANTLE design as halfcrown   Proofs and patterns only

Date				Unc/abtFDC
1831	W.W. (271)	(near FDC, minor defects, Seaby £2750)
1831	W.W. (272)	Proof in gold (Coincraft Cat. 1997) £60000
1831	W.Wyon (273)	--- --- £3000	/£5200
1832	Lead Pattern, extreme rarity edge TERTIO	£4000	----
1834	A plain edged proof	--- --- £9000	£11000 ✗

VICTORIA   *YOUNG HEAD*   Silver 38mm

1837	Incuse Pattern by Bonomi	(Auction 1987)	£2600 ✗
1837	Pattern, lead, mirror image	(Spink 1988) £650	----
1839	Proofs (279) from the sets	£1200 £2250/£3250
1844	94,248 Edge VIII :
	Star-shaped edge stops	£25 £95 £500 £900/£1800
1844	Proof with star-shaped edge stops	--- ---- £4000/£7500
1844	Cinquefoil (five leaves) stops	£25 £95 £500 £900/£1800
1845	159,192 Edge VIII	£25 £95 £550 £1500/£2000
1845	L. Skelhorn reports doubled obverse £500 offered in 1996
1846	Pattern (341) by W. Wyon	--- (1980) /£3000
1847	140,976 Edge XI	£25 £75 £400 £800/£1200
1847	8,000 UNDECIMO proof GOTHIC:
		£250 £450 £650 £1300/£1900
1847	Roy Francis pinpoints Spink-Taisei sale 1988, 1 in gold	£113,000
1847	Error edge SEPTIMO proof GOTHIC	---- -----/-----
1847	Without edge number (ESC 291)	£750 £1200/£1600
1853	460 (293) DECIMO SEPTIMO from sets £2000 £3000/£4000
1853	as previous (Cooke '98) "light scuffs otherwise FDC" £3750
1853	(Whiteaves-Scott '95) "Magnificent Gem FDC" £4250
1853	(294) Without edge number	---- £4500/£6000
1879	Return to Young Head. Offers for this exceed	£15,000 ✗

"Gothic" crowns have the obverse inscribed, at perimeter,
thus: mdcccxlvii for 1847, or mdcccliii for 1853

CROWNS

VICTORIA — *Jubilee Head* — GOLDEN JUBILEE

Reverse: ST. GEORGE and THE DRAGON · SILVER 38.61mm

Date	Mintage	Fine	V.F.	E.F.	abt. Unc/FDC
1887	173,581	£10	£20	£35	£55/£75
1887	1,084 proof	--	---	£200	£300/£400
1888	131,899 close date	£12	£30	£70	£90/£140
1888	wider date	£25	£50	£100	£150/£225
1889	1,807,223	£9	£15	£30	£45/£70
1890	997,862	£10	£20	£40	£80/£120
1891	566,394	£10	£25	£60	£90/£140
1892	451,334	£15	£30	£90	£130/£220

VICTORIA — *Old, Veiled or Widow Head*

Date	Mintage		Fine	V.F.	E.F.	abt. Unc/FDC
1893	1,312	LVI proofs from sets			£150	£250/£360
1893	497,845	LVI	£10	£30	£60	£95/£145
1893		LVII	£15	£50	£100	£165/£250
1894	144,906	LVII	£9	£30	£95	£175/£250
1894		LVIII	£9	£30	£80	£160/£240
1895	252,862	LVIII	£9	£30	£80	£160/£220
1895		LIX	£9	£30	£80	£160/£220
1896	317,599	LIX	£12	£40	£130	£250/£375
1896		LX	£9	£30		£120/£200
1897	262,118	LX	£9	£30	£90	£120/£200
1897		LXI	£10	£30	£60	£120/£200
1898	161,450	LXI	£15	£50	£150	£200/£275
1898		LXII	£9	£30	£90	£120/£180
1899	166,300	LXII	£9	£30	£90	£120/£180
1899		LXIII	£9	£30	£90	£120/£180
1900	353,356	LXIII	£15	£50	£95	£150/£250
1900		LXIV	£15	£50	£100	£175/£300

EDWARD VII

Reverse: ST. GEORGE and THE DRAGON · SILVER 38.61mm

Date	Mintage	Fine	V.F.	E.F.	abt Unc/FDC
1902	256,020	£20	£40	£60	£120/£130
1902	15,123 proof with matt surface			£60	£100/£125
1902	(noted 1999)	---	---	---	"abt.F.D.C." £115
1902	★ Pattern depicting Edward VII, robed, and on horseback				
1902	Pattern similar to the previous entry, struck in gold				

★ 1902 Style as Charles I "Tower" (Spinks 1985) £2,500

GEORGE V — *debased silver .500 fineness from 1927*

Reverse: ST. GEORGE and THE DRAGON · SILVER 38.61mm

Date	Mintage	Fine	V.F.	E.F.	abt Unc/FDC
1910	Pattern: flowing interpretation George/Dragon				
1910	Similar but date in exergue reverse (ESC 389) £3,500				
1927	15,030 proofs from the sets			£60	£90/£100
1928	9,034	£30	£60	£90	£125/£175
1928	(J. Welsh 1991)			"Gem BU/FDC"	£150
1929	4,994	£30	£60	£90	£125/£175
1930	4,847	£30	£60	£90	£130/£180
1931	4,056	£35	£70	£140	£180/£290
1932	2,395	£50	£75	£150	£200/£300
1932	4 proof (noted 1986)			"gdEF/FDC"	£950
1933	7,132	£30	£60	£95	£145/£250
1934	932	£300	£500	£1000	£1500/£---
1934	(noted 2001)	---	"EF"	£825	--/---
1934	8 proof (Coincraft Cat. '97)				£4000
1935	714,769 incuse edge lettering	£4	£9		£12/£15
1935	Superior strikings,	---	in special box		£25/£35
1935	Superior strikings,	---	without box		£20/£30
1935	2,500 silver proofs, raised edge lettering				£200/£250
1935	A few .925 silver proof incuse edge lettering				£1750
1935	★ Some; both incuse and raised, have edge lettering error				
1935	Error edge	£50	£75	£125	£250/£325
1935	30 proof struck in gold raised edge lettering £12000				
1935	A pattern - date in front of horse's head				£15,950
1936	2,473	£60	£100	£200	£300/£350
1936	3 or 4 proofs are thought to exist "guesstimate" £1600				

★ correct order of words: DECUS ET TUTAMEN ANNO REGNI

CROWNS

Date	Mintage		Fine	V.F.	E.F.	Abt. Unc/FDC.

EDWARD VIII   *.500 fine silver*   38.61mm

1936	Unofficial patterns	(Hearn)			FDC	£30
1936	(noted 2001)		---	---	"FDC"	£35
1936	Sterling silver proofs by Maklouf				FDC	£30
1937	designs similar to George VI		"guesstimate"			£75,000

GEORGE VI   *.500 fine silver*   38.61mm

1937	418,699	Coronation	£12	£18	£22/£30
1937	26,402	Proofs from the sets		---	£30/£40
1937	Proofs with special frosting (V.I.P.) 0.925 silver				£200/£250
1937	Matt, sand-blasted die, patterns		--	--	/£800

Cupro-nickel

MDCCCLI CIVIUM INDUSTRIA FLORET CIVITAS MCMLI
(1851 By the industry of its people the state flourishes 1951)

1951	1,983,540	Festival of Britain Prooflike	£4		£6/£8
1951	In box of issue, green or purple		£6		£8/£10
1951	Proofs from the sets (same striking as previous)				£6/£8
1951	Proofs with special frosting (V.I.P.) 0.925 silver				£150/£200
1951★	Patterns (or special proofs) (K.B.Coins 1990)			FDC	£450
1951	Proofs, error strike on unedged blanks				£150/£250
1951	Matt, sand-blasted die, patterns		--	--	/£800

★ Not to be confused with 'prooflike' issue; the 'specials' have finer edge lettering and are, usually, accompanied by written provenance.

ELIZABETH II

Date	Mintage		Fine	V.F.	E.F.	Abt. Unc/FDC
1953	5,962,621	Equestrian	--	£1	£2	£4/£6
1953	Edge: FAITH AND TRUST ··· BEAR UNTO YO (no 'U'):			£20	£30	£40/£50
1953	40,000	Proofs, sets and Maundy	£15		£20/£30
1953★	(K.B.Coins '94)	(Special proofs)	--		FDC £395
1953	Pattern	All-over frosting, dismal/matt			£600/£700
1953	Large date/Large emblems on cross		--		£350
1960	1,024,038	British Trades Fair	£2	£4	£6/£8
1960	70,000	Polished die specials	--	£5	£9/£16
1960★	(K.B.Coins '94)	(V.I.P. Proof)			FDC £475
1965	19,640,000	Churchill	--	--	50p	75p/£1
1965	(K.B.Coins 1990)	Satin finish "special"			FDC £560

★ Frosted detail, highly polished field; not to be confused with 'ordinary' polished die proofs: the 'specials' have finer edge lettering and would be accompanied by written provenance.

DECIMAL CROWNS (Twentyfive Pence)

	Cupro-nickel Mintage	Selected Unc	Proof from Set	Silver Proof From/to	Silver Proof Mintage
1972	7,452,100 Silver Wedding	£2	£5	£14/£20	100,000
1977	36,989,000 Silver Jubilee	£2	£5	£14/£20	377,000
1977	Selected coin in R.M. folder	£4	--		
1980	Queen Mother's 80th Birthday:				
1980	9,477,513	£2	£6	£22/£25	83,672
1980	Selected coin in R.M. folder	£5	--		
1981	Royal Wedding:				
1981	27,360,279	£2	£6	£25/£35	218,142
1981	Selected coin in R.M. folder	£5	--		
1989	FOUR-CROWN-COLLECTION of silver proofs £125				
	(The Case, Booklet and Certificate should be preserved)				

1, 2, 5 and 10 cents	inverted reverse	£900
1, 2, 5 and 10 cents restrikes	upright reverse	£300

VICTORIA

DECIMAL 'FARTHING' of 1854   1/1000 of £1   a MILLE
1854 (noted 94) "As struck" MODEL MILLE, GOTHIC HEAD, £125
1854 (noted 1996)   "abtVF" £89   "gdVF" £99   - - - -

VICTORIA PATTERNS of 1857 BRITANNIA Reverse BRONZE

	Legend above Britannia:	Legend below Britannia:	
A)	ONE CENT	MDCCCLVII	16.5mm
B)	HALF FARTHING	ONE CENTIME	17.0mm
C)	TWO CENTS	MDCCCLVII	22.0mm
D)	ONE FARTHING	TWO CENTIMES	22.0mm
E)	FIVE CENTS	MDCCCLVII	27.0mm
F)	DECIMAL HALFPENNY	5 CENTIMES	27.5mm
G)	DECIMAL HALFPENNY	MDCCCLVII	27.0mm
H)	FIVE FARTHINGS	10 CENTIMES	33.5mm
H)	(Noted 1989 about V.F.)	FIVE FARTHINGS	£125
I)	DECIMAL PENNY ONE TENTH OF A SHILLING		32.5mm
J)	TEN CENTS	ONE TENTH OF A SHILLING	32.5mm

VICTORIA PATTERNS of 1859 DATE BELOW HEAD BRONZE

K)	HALF DECIMAL PENNY in wreath oak leaves/acorns	27mm
L)	HALF DECIMAL PENNY ONE TWENTIETH SHILLING	27mm
M)	ONE DECIMAL PENNY in wreath oak leaves/acorns	32mm
M)	(Noted 1986 E.F.) Cupro-nickel and tin	£400
N)	ONE TENTH OF DECIMAL SHILLING A PENNY	32mm
O)	★ DECIMAL PENNY ★ ONE TENTH OF A SHILLING	32mm
O2)	Has larger lettering and date between ornaments	32mm
O2)	(Noted 1986 E.F.) Nickel-bronze	£250
P)	ONE DECIMAL PENNY wreath laurel leaves/berries	32mm
Q)	As P) but wreath half palm leaves, half oak leaves	32mm
R)	ONE DECIMAL PENNY lion, shield, flags, bee-hive	32mm
S)	DECIMAL PENNY crown, trident, laurel/oak wreath	32mm
	See trident of 1961 2 CENTS	

VICTORIA PATTERNS of 1859 SIZE REDUCED BRONZE

T)	DECIMAL HALF PENNY	laurel wreath with berries
U)	DECIMAL HALF PENNY	half laurel, half oak, crown
V)	DECIMAL HALF PENNY	complete circle of palm leaves
W)	ONE DECIMAL PENNY in exergue	lion and palm tree
X)	DECIMAL 1 PENNY	below large trident with dolphins
Y)	ONE PENNY Una and the Lion DECIMAL in exergue	
Z)	ONE DECIMAL PENNY	wreath alternating oak & laurel
Z2)	ONE DECIMAL PENNY	wreath half oak, half laurel
Z3)	Roses, Shamrocks, Thistles around ONE DECIMAL PENNY	

First three 19.5 mm;   W) to Z3) 27 mm.
Coins without date, or without denomination, not listed.

VICTORIA Silver Patterns 1848 ONE TENTH OF A POUND 27 mm

1)	Trident, wreath of oak leaves, 100 MILLES -	ONE DECADE	
2)	Trident, wreath of oak leaves, 100 MILLES -	ONE CENTUM	
3)	Trident - wreath of oak leaves -	ONE FLORIN	
4)	Royal cypher VR - emblems intertwined -	ONE DECADE	
4)	(noted 1988) ONE DECADE "as struck"	£725	
5)	Royal cypher VR - emblems intertwined -	ONE CENTUM	
5)	(Spink 1988) ONE CENTUM "gdEF"	£695	
6)	Royal cypher VR - emblems intertwined -	ONE FLORIN	
7)	Cruciform shields - rose at centre, below -	ONE DIME	
	Each of the seven with three different obverses (!)		
8)	Cruciform shields - laureate head -	date below	
9)	Cruciform shields - plain hair binding -	date below	
10)	1848 Cruciform shields - crowned bust -	Godless florin	
11)	1851 As 1848 but in Gothic style:	the date as mdcccli	
	Values for GODLESS and GOTHIC florins on page 33		

ELIZABETH II   Decimal Patterns

1 CENT - 1961 - ER - ONE DECIMAL PENNY -	Bronze 20mm	
2 CENTS - crown, ornamented trident - 1961 -	Bronze 25mm	
Set of 1961 comprising 1, 2, 5, 10, 20 and 50 cents sold at		
Sotheby's 1986 for £2,400 plus buyers premium and VAT		
Aluminium quarter penny - Tudor Rose over 1/4 -	20mm	
Bronze half penny - Welsh Dragon over 1/2 -	17mm	
Bronze penny - Scottish Lion, St Andrews Cross -	20mm	
Bronze two pence - Britannia over large 2 -	26mm	
Cupro-nickel five pence - Three Crowns over 5 -	23mm	
Cupro-nickel ten pence - St George and The Dragon -	28mm	
Cupro-nickel twenty pence - Gartered Royal Arms -	36mm	
(in 1982, a decimal pattern for 20p dated 1963 @	£1,500)	
(in 1986, full set of decimal patterns dated 1963 @	£4,500)	
(in 1986, uniface set artist's copies at Spink's @	£900)	

IN 1982 THE WORD 'NEW' WAS DISCONTINUED

Half New Penny — BRONZE 17mm

Year		Selected Unc/Proof	Year		Selected Unc/Proof	THE ROYAL CROWN Year		Selected Unc/Proof
1971	1,394,188,250	20p/£2	1976	412,172,000	50p/£2	1982		15p/£2
1971	Double headed	£200	1977		20p/£2	1983	7,600,000	25p/£2
1972	Proof ex-set	---/£5	1978	59,532,000	25p/£2			From sets
1973	365,680,000	50p/£2	1979		20p/£2	1984	158,820	£2/£3
1974	365,448,000	50p/£2	1980		50p/£2			Demonetized 31/12/84
1975	197,600,000	50p/£2	1981	46,748,000	60p/£2			

One New Penny — BRONZE 20mm to 1991

A PORTCULLIS WITH CHAINS ROYALLY CROWNED

Plated Steel, magnetic, 1992 — non-magnetic 1998

Year		Selected Unc/Proof	Year		Selected Unc/Proof	Year	Selected Unc/Proof
1971	1,521,666,250	15p/£2	1982		60p/£2	Now "magnetic" until 1998	
1972	Proof from set	---/£5	1983	243,002,000	£1/£3	1992	10p/£2
1973	280,196,000	£1/£3	1984	154,759,625	£1/£3	1993	10p/£2
1974	330,892,000	£1/£3	1985	200,605,245	50p/£2	1994	10p/£2
1975	221,604,000	£1/£3	1986	369,989,130	50p/£2	1995	10p/£2
1976	241,800,000	£1/£3	1987	499,946,000	50p/£2	1996	10p/£2
1977	285,430,000	£1/£3	1988	793,492,000	50p/£2	1997	10p/£2
1978	292,770,000	£1/£3	1989	532,532,000	50p/£2	1998	New portrait
1979	459,000,000	£1/£3	1990		50p/£2	1999	....
1980	416,304,000	£1/£3	1991		50p/£2	2000	....
1981	301,800,000	£1/£3	1992		£5/£5	2001	....
						2002	....

Two New Pence — BRONZE 26mm to 1991

THE BADGE OF THE PRINCE OF WALES

Plated Steel, magnetic, 1992 — non-magnetic 1998

Year		Selected Unc/Proof	Year		Selected Unc/Proof	Year	Selected Unc/Proof
1971	1,454,856,250	15p/£2	1983	637,100	£3/£2	Now "magnetic" until 1998	
1972, 1973, 1974		---/£5	1983**	with old rev.		1992	25p/£2
1975	145,545,000	75p/£2	1984	158,820	£1/£2	1993	25p/£2
1976	181,379,000	75p/£2	1985	107,113,000	50p/£2	1994	25p/£2
1977	109,261,000	25p/£2	1986	168,967,500	50p/£2	1995	10p/£2
1978	189,658,000	£1/£3	1987	218,100,750	50p/£2	1996	10p/£2
1979	260,200,000	30p/£2	1988	419,889,000	50p/£2	1997	10p/£2
1980	408,527,000	25p/£2	1989	292,093,000	50p/£2	1998	New portrait
1981	353,191,000	30p/£2	1990		25p/£2	1999	....
1981	Double "tail"	£125	1991		25p/£2	2000	....
1982	205,000	£4/£2	1992		£5/£5	2001	....
						2002	....

1983**	two authenticated examples, so far, still inscribed 'NEW'.
1983**	"Uncertain" value · catalogued from £250 to £1,500
1985	New MAKLOUF portrait of The Queen (see page 28)
1992	The twopence became "magnetic" being copper-plated steel.
1998	New RANK-BROADLEY portrait of The Queen (page 28)
1998	Rotated die · authenticated by R.M. -ref: B. Simpson Esq.

Five Pence

A THISTLE ROYALLY CROWNED

23.59mm 1968-1990 | 18mm 1990 onwards

Year	Mintage	Selected Unc/	Proof★
1968	98,868,250	50p/	--
1969	119,270,000	75p/	--
1970	225,948,525	75p/	--
1971	81,783,475	75p/	£2
1972★		---/	£6
1973★		---/	£6
1974★		---/	£6
1975	86,550,000	50p/	£2
1976★		---/	£4
1977	24,308,000	35p/	£2
1978	61,000,000	50p/	£3
1979	155,456,000	75p/	£3

Year	Mintage	Selected Unc/	Proof★
1980	220,566,000	£1/	£3
1981★		--/	£6
1982★	205,000	£5/	£5
1983★	637,100	£5/	£5
1984★	158,820	£3/	£5
1985★	178,375	£3/	£4
1986★		£2/	£3
1987	48,220,000	£1/	£2
1988	120,744,610	£1/	£2
1989	101,406,000	£1/	£3
1990★		£3/	£4
1990 Smaller/18mm		20p/	£2
1990 35,000 silver			
'pair' both sizes			£25
1990 20,000 piedfort			£30

Year	Selected Unc/	Proof★
1991	20p/	£2
1992	20p/	£2
1993	50p/	£3
1994	50p/	£2
1995	---/	£2
1996	---/	£2
1996 Silver proof		£15
1997	---/	£2
1998	---/	£3
1999	---/	£3
2000	---/	£3
2001	---/	---
2002	---/	---

Ten Pence

CUPRO-NICKEL · A LION PASSANT GUARDANT ROYALLY CROWNED

28.5mm 1968-1990 | 24.5mm 1990 onwards

Year	Mintage	Selected Unc/	Proof★
1968	336,143,250	£1/	--
1969	314,008,000	£2/	--
1970	133,571,000	£3/	--
1971	63,205,000	£3/	£4
1972	Proof from set	--/	£5
1973	152,174,000	£2/	£4
1974	92,741,000	£2/	£4
1975	181,559,000	£2/	£4
1976	228,220,000	£2/	£4
1977	59,323,000	£2/	£3
1978	Proof from set	--/	£6

The florin/two shilling/28.5mm 'tenpence' piece was demonetized 30th June, 1993

Year	Mintage	Selected Unc/	Proof★
1979	115,457,000	£2/	£4
1980	88,650,000	£2/	£4
1981	3,487,000	£3/	£5
1982★	205,000	£5/	£6
1983★	637,100	£6/	£7
1984★	158,820	£3/	£4
1985★	178,375	£3/	£4
1986★		£2/	£3
1987	172,425	£2/	£3
1988★		£2/	£3
1989★		£3/	£4
1990★		£4/	£6
1991★		£4/	£6
1992★		£4/	£6
Smaller 24.5mm			
1992		£3/	£4

Year	Selected Unc/	Proof★
1992 Silver Proof		
'pair' both sizes		£30
1992 Silver Proof		£10
1992 Piedfort		£50
1993 ★	£5/	£4
1994 ★	£4/	£4
1995	£3/	£4
1996	£2/	£3
1996 Silver proof		£15
1997	£2/	£3
1998 ★	---/	£3
1999 ★	---/	£3
2000	---/	£3
2001	---/	---
2002	---/	---

K.A.Mallett Esq reports a 1968 10p with dies rotated 90°; the Royal Mint confirms coin genuine and acknowledges an unobserved loose holding collar.

★ Indicates coins removed from sets.

TWENTY PENCE
A DOUBLE ROSE ROYALLY CROWNED
CUPRO-NICKEL 21.4mm

Year	Mintage	Selected Unc/Proof★	Year	Selected Unc/Proof★
1982	740,815,000	£1/ £6	1993★★	£1/ £3
1982	25,000 Piedfort	/£50	1994	£1/ £2
1983	158,463,000	£1/ £5	1995	50p/ £1
1984	65,350,965	£1/ £5	1996	50p/ £1
1985	74,273,699	£1/ £5	1996 Silver	/£15
1986	From the sets	£1/ £5	1997	50p/ £1
1987	137,450,000	£1/ £5	1998	/ £3
1988	38,038,344	£1/ £4	1999	/ £3
1989	109,128,890	£1/ £4	2000	/ £3
1990		£1/ £5	2001	
1991		£1/ £5	2002	
1992		£1/ £4	2003	

★★ R. Colliass Esq reports, and the Royal Mint confirms, a steel blank intended for a 1p struck in error with the dies of the of the 1993 20p (source 1995)

FIFTY PENCE
CUPRO-NICKEL 30 mm

Proofs, are those taken from the sets unless otherwise indicated.

Year	Mintage	Selected Unc/Proof	Year		Sel.Unc/Proof		Sel.Unc/Proof
1969	188,400,000	£3/ £4	1981	Double "tail"	£200	Silver ★★★	£30
1969	Double "head"	£150	1982	51,312,000	£2/ £5	Piedfort ★★★	£60
1970	19,461,000	£2/ £5	1983	62,824,904	£2/ £5	Gold ★★★	£500
1971	and 1972	- -/ £6	1984	158,820	£2/ £5	1994 ex-sets	£3/ £6
1973	89,775,000	£3/ - -	1985	679,603	£2/ £5	1995 ex-sets	£4/ £6
Proofs	356,616 cased	£4	1986		£2/ £5	1996 ex-sets	£3/ £6
Piedfort	(about 20)	£2,500	1987	172,425	£2/ £5	1996 Silver	/£15
1974	and 1975	- -/ £5	1988		£3/ £5	1997 ex-sets	£3/ £6
1976	43,746,500	£3/ £6	1989		£3/ £5	1997 new size 27.3mm	
1977	49,536,000	£3/ £6	1990		£3/ £6	1997	- - -/ - - -
1978	72,005,500	£3/ £6	1991		£5/ £9	1998	NEW EFFIGY
1979	58,680,000	£3/ £6	1992		£4/ £5		by Ian Rank-Broadley
1980	89,086,000	£3/ £6	1993		£4/ £4		see page 28
1981	74,002,000	£2/ £4	1992/93 ★★★		£5/ £9		

1973 (currency and proofs) EEC Commemoratives
1992/1993 ★★★ Design to commemmorate Britain's Presidency/Council of Ministers

Year	Description	Selected Unc./Proof	Uncirc. Folder	Silver Proof	Silver Piedfort	Gold
1994	"D-Day"	£1/£5	£5	£40	£75	£450
1997	10,000 27.3mm New Size	£1/£4	- - -	£26.75	£50	- - - -
1997	Cased Pairs 30mm and 27.3mm	- - -/ - - -	- - -	£47.50	- - -	- - - -
1998	Traditional Britannia reverse	£2/ £3	- - -	- - -	- - -	- - - -
1998	25 Year Commem. of EU · 12 stars	£2/ £5	- - -	£24.95	£45	£249
1998	Pair · Britannia and EU	£5.45/	- - -	- - -	- - -	- - - -
1998	50th Anniversary of N.H.S.	50p/£5	£5	£24.95	£45	£249
1998	Pair · EU and N.H.S.	- - -/ - - -	- - -	£49.90	- - -	- - - -
1999	Traditional Britannia reverse	£2/ £3				
2000	150 years Public Libraries	50p/ £3	£5	£24.95	£46	£249
2000	Traditional Britannia reverse	£2/ £3				
2001	Traditional Britannia reverse	£2/ £3				
2002						

Pale-yellow mixture of metals · 22.5 mm dia. · 3.1 mm thick · has grained (milled) edge, with incuse (struck in) lettering. England and Northern Ireland variants read: DECUS ET TUTAMEN (An Ornament and a Safeguard) first used to prevent the clipping of coins.

Scotland: NEMO ME IMPUNE LACESSIT: (No One Provokes Me with Impunity)

For Wales: PLEIDOL WYF I'M GWALD :   (True Am I to My Country)

Date	Mintage		Unc./Proof
1983	434,000,000	Royal Coat of Arms general issue	£3/£5
1983	484,900	Selected general issue in wallet	£6/ - -
1983	50,000	Sterling silver (.925) proofs	£25
1983	10,000	Silver Piedfort proofs.	£125
1984	110,000,000	Thistle for Scotland general issue	£2/£5
1984	27,960	Selected general issue in wallet	£6/ - -
1984	44,855	Sterling silver (.925) proofs	£20
1984	15,000	Silver Piedfort proofs.	£45
1985	178,000,000	Leek for Wales general issue	£3/£5
1985		Selected general issue in wallet	£6/ - -
1985	50,000	Sterling silver (.925) proofs	£20
1985	15,000	Silver Piedfort proofs.	£45
1986	Not revealed	Flax Plant for Northern Ireland	£2/£5
		Selected general issue in wallet	£6/ - -
1986	50,000	Sterling silver (.925) proofs	£25
1986	15,000	Silver Piedfort proofs.	£45
1987		An Oak Tree for general issue	£2/£5
		Selected general issue in wallet	£6/ - -
1987	50,000	Sterling silver (.925) proofs	£25
1987	15,000	Silver Piedfort proofs.	£45
1988		The Royal Arms of H.M. The Queen	£3/£5
		Selected general issue in wallet	£6/ - -
1988	50,000	Sterling silver (.925) proofs	£25
1988	15,000	Silver Piedfort proofs.	£45
1989		Re-appearance of the Thistle Pound	£3/£5
		Selected general issue in wallet	£6/ - -
1989	25,000	Sterling silver (.925) proofs	£20
1989	10,000	Silver Piedfort proofs.	£50
1990		Re-appearance of the Leek Pound	£2/£4
1990	25,000	Sterling silver (.925) proofs	£20
1991		Re-appearance of the Flax Pound	£2/£4
1991	25,000	Sterling silver (.925) proofs	£20
1992		General Issue (Oak Tree)	£2/£4
1992	25,000	Sterling silver (.925) proofs	£20
1993		General Issue · Royal Arms	£2/£4
1993	25,000	Sterling silver (.925) proofs	£30
1993	12,500	Silver Peidfort proofs	£50

1984 - 1987   4 coin silver proof collection in red leather case £60
1984 - 1987   4 coin silver piedfort proof collection   £125

Mr. Whitehead says he has found a 1988 £1 bearing the FLAX PLANT. He cannot have confused one plant with another because the 'correct' issue for 1988 is a very severe non-flowering shield bearing the ROYAL ARMS. Although "rather worn" this must be considered a GOOD FIND.

ISSUE PRICE

(Issue Price or Selected/Uncirculated Values · 28.4mm · 12 grams)

1994		FIRST of NEW SERIES	Selected Unc/Proof
		Scottish Lion Rampant	£2/ £5
1994	25,000	Sterling silver (.925) proofs	£30
1994	12,500	Silver Piedfort proofs	£50
1994		Presentation folder, nickel-brass	£3/ ---
1995		Welsh Dragon · nickel-brass:	£3/ £5
		Presentation folder · English text	£4/ ---
		Presentation folder · text in Welsh	£5/ ---
1995	25,000	Sterling silver (.925) proofs	£25
1995	12,500	Silver Piedfort proofs	£50
1996		N. Ireland Celtic Cross	£2/ £4
1996		Presentation folder, nickel-brass	£4/ ---
1996	25,000	Sterling silver (.925) proofs	£25
1996	12,500	Silver Piedfort proofs	£50
1997		English: Three Lions *passant guardant*	£2/ £4
1997		Presentation folder, nickel-brass	£4.50
1997	30,000	Sterling silver (.925) proofs	£25
1997	10,000	Silver Piedfort proofs	£50

NEW PORTRAIT OF H.M. THE QUEEN by Ian Rank-Broadley

		Selected Unc/Proof	Uncirc. Folder	Silver Proof	Silver Piedfort	Philatelic (PNCs) Numismatic Covers	
1998	The Royal Arms	£2/ £6	£4.50	£25	£45	30,000 ·	£12.95
1999	Scottish Lion	£2/ £6	£4.50	£25	£45	40,000 ·	£12.95
2000	Welsh Dragon	£2/ £4	£4.50	£25	£50		£12.95
2001	Broighter Collar · N.I.	£2/ £4	£4.50	£26	£50		£12.95

1986 COMMEMORATING EDINBURGH COMMONWEALTH GAMES

Thistle, Wreath, Cross of St.Andrew	£3	Selected in wallet	£6
125,000 Nickel-brass proofs	£6	58,881 .500 silver	£15
59,779 925 silver proofs	£25	3,277 gold proofs	£200

1989 COMMEMORATING 300th ANNIVERSARY BILL OF RIGHTS

William & Mary. Not for general issue, but still legal tender.

Bill of Rights	£4	Selected in wallet	£5
Claim of Right	£8	Selected in wallet	£10
		Pair, as picture, selected, in Official blister-pack	£16
25,000 each	Bill and Claim proofs in silver singles		£24
10,000 pairs	Bill AND Claim proofs, silver, piedfort, pairs		£90

1994 COMMEMORATING TERCENTENARY of THE BANK OF ENGLAND

Edge: SIC VOS NON VOBIS (Thus you labour but not for yourselves)
Uncirculated £3 · Blister-pack £5 · Proofs from sets £6
Silver proof, 27,957, £25 · Silver Proof Piedfort £50
Gold 'TWO POUNDS' £400 · error not showing value £700

1995 WORLD WAR II · DOVE OF PEACE · edge: IN PEACE GOODWILL

Uncirculated £3 · Blister-pack £4 · Proofs from sets £6
Silver Proof 50,000, £30 · Piedfort, 10,000, £50 · Gold Proof, £375

(28.4mm · 12 grams)

1995 UNITED NATIONS 50th ANNIVERSARY · 1945 - 1995
Uncirculated £3 · Proof £6 · Folder £5 · Silver Proof, 175,000, £30
Silver Proof Piedfort 10,000 £50 · Gold Proof 17,500 £350

1996 EUROPEAN FOOTBALL CHAMPIONSHIP
Uncirculated £3 · Selected in Folder £5 · Proof £6
Silver Proof 50,000 £27 · Piedfort 10,000 £55 · Gold 2,098 £295
Missing designer's initials (like old-time laces) £9

1997 GENERAL CIRCULATION · FIRST TWO-TONE COIN
Uncirculated £3 · Selected in Folder £6 · Proof £6
Silver Proof (has the outer ring plated with ·999 gold) 40,000 £29
Silver Proof Piedfort 10,000 £50
Gold Proof (using 22 carat red gold outer/yellow gold inner) 2,500 £325

1997 release of TWO-TONE ROYAL MINT TRIAL dated 1994
Descriptive card folder featuring four items: Inner and Outer Blanks;
The inner combined with Edge Lettered Outer; and the Finished Coin · £20

1998 BRITISH INDUSTRY · edge: STANDING on the SHOULDERS of GIANTS
New effigy of H.M. The Queen by Ian Rank-Broadley Rev. by Bruce Rushin
Commenced general circulation on Monday 15th June, 1998
Uncirculated £4 · Proof £6 · Folder £6 · Silver Proof 25,000, £29
Silver Proof Piedfort 10,000 £50
Gold Proof (using 22 carat red gold outer/yellow gold inner) 2,500 £325

1999 RUGBY WORLD CUP TOURNAMENT · edge: RUGBY WORLD CUP 1999
Aerial representation of Stadium, Ball and Goal Posts
Uncirculated £3 · Proof £6 · Folder £6 · Silver Proof 25,000, £29
Silver Proof Piedfort · Colour Producing Holography · 10,000 £50
Gold Proof (using 22 carat red gold outer/yellow gold inner) 2,000 £325

2000 BRITISH INDUSTRY · edge: STANDING on the SHOULDERS of GIANTS
Bruce Rushkin's reverse design repeated

2001 MARCONI · edge: WIRELESS BRIDGES THE ATLANTIC · MARCONI 1901
Decorative Radio Waves emanating from a spark of electricity · Robert Evans
Uncirculated £3 · Folder £7 · Silver Proof 25,000, £29
Gold Proof (using 22 carat red gold outer/yellow gold inner) 2,500 £295

2001 BRITISH INDUSTRY · edge: STANDING on the SHOULDERS of GIANTS
Bruce Rushkin's reverse design repeated

Legal Tender for £5 · 38.61mm · 28.28 grams

1990 COMMEMORATING THE QUEEN MOTHER's 90th BIRTHDAY
Interlaced Es · Rose and Thistle · Uncirculated £8
Pack £10 · Silver Proofs 56,102, £38 · Gold Proofs 2,500, £600

1993 THE CORONATION ANNIVERSARY 1953/1993
Queen's 1953 portrait encircled by mounted trumpeters/swords/sceptres
Selected Unc. £7 · Official Pack £10 · Cupro-nickel Proofs £9
Silver Proofs 100,000 £32 · Gold Proofs 2,500 £650

1996 COMMEMORATING H.M. THE QUEEN'S 70th BIRTHDAY
Edge: VIVAT REGINA ELIZABETHA
Selected Unc. £7 · Official Pack £10 · Cupro-nickel Proofs £12
Silver Proofs 70,000 £32 · Gold Proofs 2,127 £650

1997 COMMEMORATING THE GOLDEN WEDDING
Princess Elizabeth to Lieutenant Phillip Mountbatten 20th Nov. 1947
Selected Unc. £7 · Official Pack £10 · Cupro-nickel Proofs £12
Silver Proofs 75,000 £32 · Gold Proofs 2,750 £650

1998 COMMEMORATING 50th BIRTHDAY H.R.H. The Prince of Wales
New Effigy of H.M. The Queen by Ian Rank Broadley · Rev. by Michael Noakes
Selected Unc. £7 · Official Pack £10 · Cupro-nickel Proofs £12
Silver Proofs 35,000 £32 · Gold Proofs 2,000 £600

1999 PRINCESS DIANA COMMEMORATIVE · July 1st, 1999
Selected Unc. £7 · Official Pack £10 · PNC postmark 1/1/99 £16
Cu-nickel Proof £12 · Silv. Proof 350,000 £32 · Gold Proof 7,500 £595

1999 · 2000 MILLENNIUM · edge: What's Past is Prologue ("The Tempest")
Selected Unc. £7 · Official Pack £10 · Cupro-nickel Proof £12
Silver Proof 100,000 £35 · Gold Proof 2,500 £600

2000 COMMEMORATING THE QUEEN MOTHER'S 100th BIRTHDAY
Selected Unc. £6 · Official Pack £10 · PNC £15.95
Silver Proof £35 · Silver Piedfort Proof 20,000 £68 · Gold 3,000 £495
Proof Crown and £5 note with prefix QM10-0 £50

2001 VICTORIAN ANNIVERSARY CROWN (£5)
Selected Unc. £6 · Official Pack £10 · PNC £15.95
Silver Proof £35 · Gold 3,500 £525

GEORGE IV

1826	140 sets	(11)	Farthing to five pounds	£17,000/£20,000
	(noted 2000)		the above plus Maundy	£18,500

WILLIAM IV

1831	145 sets	(14)	Maundy replaces £5	£12,500/£16,500
	Silver only	(8)	(Spink 1988) E.F. £4,400	------

VICTORIA

1839	300 sets	(15)	in spade shaped case which includes:	
			the Una-and-The-Lion gold £5	£25,000/£28,000
1853	460	(16)	Quarter-farthing to Gothic 5/-	£20,000/£25,000
1853	(Bonhams 1998)			£18,400
1887	797 sets	(11)	unofficial cases 3d to £5	£4,500/ £5,500
1887	287 sets		3d to 5/-	£750/ £950
1893	773 sets	(10)	rarely intact 3d to £5	£4,500/ £6,500
1893	Short set of six silver coins		3d to 5/-	£900/ £1,200

EDWARD VII

1902	8,066 sets	(13)	Maundy 1d to £5 (matt)	£1,000/ £1,500
1902	7,057 sets	(11)	Maundy 1d to sovereign	£400/ £550

GEORGE V

1911	2,812 sets	(12)	Maundy 1d to £5	£2,000 £2,500
1911	(noted 1999)	(12)	"FDC in case of issue, fabulous"	£2,250
1911	952 sets	(10)	Maundy 1d to sovereign	£600/ £750
1911	2,241 sets	(8)	Maundy penny to half-crown	£250/ £350
1927	15,030 sets	(6)	3d to crown	£200/ £250

GEORGE VI

1937	5,501 sets	(4)	Half-sovereign to £5	£1,500/£1,800
1937	26,402 sets	(15)	Farthing to crown + Maundy	£90/ £120
1950	17,513 sets	(9)	Farthing to half-crown	£50/ £65
1951	20,000 sets	(10)	Farthing to crown	£50/ £75

ELIZABETH II

1953	40,000 sets	(10)	Farthing to crown (5/-)	£40/ £60
1953		★	A large number of sets in plastic wallet (9)	£8/ £10
1968		★	Decimal souvenir sets, mixed dates in folder	£1/ £3
1970	750,000	Last Sterling	½d to 2/6d + medallion	£10/ £15

★ non-proof, selected currency coins
(noted 2000 John Satin) plastic set with 1 + B "unc" £10

F.D.C. from/to

1971	350,000	(6) ★	half to 50p	£10/£12
1972	150,000	(7) ★	plus Crown	£10/£12
1973	100,000	(6) ★	half to EEC 50p	£7/ £9
1974	100,000	(6) ★	half to 50p	£6/£10
1975	100,000	(6) ★	half to 50p	£7/ £9
1976	100,000	(6) ★	half to 50p	£7/ £9
1977	193,000	(7) ★	Jubilee Crown	£10/£14
1978	88,100	(6) ★	half to 50p	£12/£16
1979	81,000	(6) ★	half to 50p	£12/£18
1980	10,000	(4)	half-sov to £5	£850
1980	143,400	(6) ★	half to 50p	£5/£10
1981	5,000	(9)	½p to gold £5	£600
1981	2,500	(2)	crown & sov.	£90/£140
1981	100,300	(6) ★	half to 50p	£5/£10
1982	2,500	(4)	half-sov to £5	£800
1982	106,800	(7) ★	plus new 20p	£5/£10
1982	205,000	(7)	Uncirc in folder	£3/ £5
1983	12,500	(3)	half-sov, sov, £2	£300
1983	107,800	(8) ★	plus 20p & £1	£8/£14
1983	637,100	(8)	Uncirc in folder	£5/ £6
1984	7,095	(3)	half-sov, sov, £5	£600
1984	125,000	(8) ★	Scottish £1	£8/£14
1984	158,820	(8)	Uncirc in folder	£5/ £6

ISSUE PRICE

1985	125,000	(7) ★ 1p to Welsh £1 Maklouf portrait, blue leatherette case	£18.75
		de-luxe red leather case	£25.75
1985		(7) Uncirc in folder	£4.75
1986	125,000	(8) ★ N.I. £1 & C/wealth £2, in blue leatherette case	£21.25
		In de-luxe red leather case	£28.25
1986		(8) Uncirc in folder	£7.95

GEORGE III

(Page 1 refers) "Collectors George III Coins" is available @ £4.50. Farthings, Halfpennies, Pennies, Twopences, Three, Four, Five, Six, Nine, Ten, Eighteen and Thirty Pences; One, Two, Three and Six Shillings; Quarter, Third, Half, One, Two and Five Guineas; Half, One, Two and Five Sovereigns; Five Pounds; Dollars, Crowns and Tokens.

ISSUE PRICE

1987	125,000	(7) ★ 1p to English Oak £1	
		in blue leatherette case	£18.95
		In de-luxe red leather case	£25.95
1987		(7) Uncirc in folder	£5.25
1988	125,000	(7) ★ 1p to Royal Arms £1	
		in blue leatherette case	£18.95
		in de-luxe red leather case	£25.95
1988		(7) Uncirc in folder	£5.25
1989	125,000	(8) ★ 1p to 'Orange' £2 x 2	
		in blue leatherette case	£22.95
		in de-luxe red leather case	£29.95
1989		(8) Uncirc in folder	£5.75
1989	Boy/Girl Baby Packs in Blue/Pink		£9.95
1990	100,000	(8) ★ 1p, (both 5p), 50p to Welsh £1 :	
		in blue leatherette case	£21.95
		in de-luxe red leather case	£28.95
1990		(8) Uncirc in folder	£6.25
1990	Boy/Girl Baby Packs in Blue/Pink		£9.95
1991	100,000	(7) ★ 1p, to N.I. £1	
		in blue leatherette case	£23.50
		in de-luxe red leather case	£30.60
1991		(8) Uncirc in folder	£7.10
1991		Baby Packs	£11.20
1991		L.s.d. set (dated 1967)	£14.25
1992	100,000	(9) ★ 1p, (10p x 2), (50p x 2) to £1	
		in blue leatherette case	£27.50
		in de-luxe red leather case	£34.50
1992		(9) uncirc in folder	£8.75
1992		Baby Packs	£13.95
1992		Wedding Pack	£13.95
1993	100,000	(8) ★ 1p to £5	
1993		in blue leatherette case	£28.75
		in de-luxe red leather case	£35.50
1993		(8) uncirc 1p to £1 (50p x 2)	£8.75
1993		Baby Gift Set	£13.95
1993		Wedding Collection	£16.50
1994	100,000	(8) ★ 1p to £1	
1994		in blue leatherette case	£24.75
		in de-luxe red leather case	£32.50
1994		(8) uncirc in folder	£8.75
1994		Baby Gift Set	£13.95
1994		Wedding Collection	£14.95
1995	100,000	(8) ★ 1p to £1	
1995		in blue leatherette case	£24.75
		In de-luxe red leather case	£32.50

ISSUE PRICE

1995		(8) uncirc in folder	£8.75
1995		Baby Gift Set	£13.95
1995		Wedding Collection	£14.95
1996	100,000	(9) ★ 1p to £5	
		in blue leatherette case	£29.75
		in de-luxe red leather case	£37.50
1996		(8) 1p to £1 in folder	£9.50
1996		Wedding Collection/Baby Gift each	£14.95
1996		LSD mixed/Decimal 1996 set	£25.00
1997	100,000	(10) ★ 1p to £5 (50p x 2)	
		in blue leatherette case	£32.50
		in de-luxe red leather case	£39.50
1997		(9) 1p to £2 (50p x 2)	£10.95
1997		Wedding Collection/Baby Gift each	£14.95
1998	100,000	(10) ★ 1p to £5 (50p x 2)	
		in blue leatherette case	£33.00
		in de-luxe red leather case	£40.00
1998		(9) 1p to £2 (50p x 2)	£10.95
1998		Wedding Collection/Baby Gift each	£14.95
1999	100,000	(9) 1p to £5 proofs	
		in blue leatherette case	£33.95
		in de-luxe red leather case	£39.95
1999		(8) 1p to £2 uncirculated	£10.95
1999		Wedding Collection/Baby Gift each	£14.95
2000	100,000	(10) ★ 1p to £5 (50p x 2)	
		Standard Proof Set	£29.95
		De-luxe Proof Set	£39.95
		Executive (10,000)	£69.95
2000		(9) 1p to £2 uncirculated	£11.50
2000		Wedding Collection/Baby Gift each	£15.95
2001	100,000	(10) ★ 1p to £5 (50p x 2)	
		Standard Proof Set	£33.50
		All occasion Gift Proof Set	£42.50
		De-luxe Proof Set	£47.50
		Executive (10,000)	£74.50
2001		(9) 1p to £2 uncirculated	£13.75
2001		Wedding Collection/Baby Gift each	£17.50
2002			